KIM MARSHALL

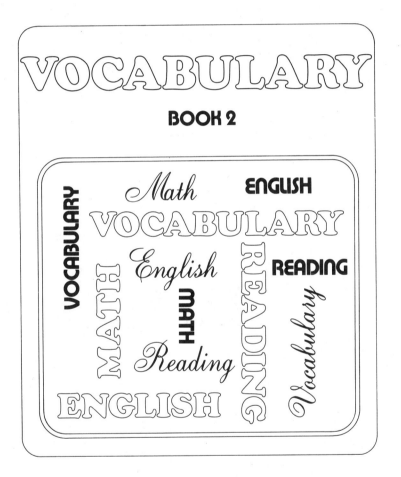

VOCABULARY

BOOK 2

Math ENGLISH
VOCABULARY
English READING
MATH
VOCABULARY MATH
Reading
ENGLISH READING Vocabulary

Educators Publishing Service, Inc.
31 Smith Place, Cambridge, MA 02138-1000

March, 1994 Printing

Acknowledgments

Without the frank comments of my students in the Martin Luther King School in Boston between 1970 and 1975, this book would not be what it is today. My students gave me new insights every day, and they deserve much credit for the sequencing, organization, and the way skills are broken down and presented in the book. I would also like to thank my wife, Rhoda Schneider, for her unceasing and invaluable support over the last ten years.

To the Student

Vocabulary — Book 1 and *Vocabulary — Book 2* are designed to improve your spelling and to broaden your vocabulary. Each book contains eighteen units of words which were chosen to be interesting and useful to you in school and in the world around you. At the front of each book is a complete list of all nine hundred words covered in the program and the units in which they appear. This is *Book 2.* It can be used alone or in conjunction with *Book 1.* The books are complementary rather than sequential.

Every unit introduces twenty-five words, some fairly easy, some more difficult. Because there are more difficult words as you move into the higher units, *Book 2* may be a little harder than *Book 1.* But the words in both books are defined with short, clear meanings which are less complicated than dictionary definitions. It is important for you to be able to spell the words and understand what they mean. If you want to know more formal, complete definitions, or more than one meaning for a word, use a dictionary.

Each unit has five pages of exercises to help you learn the spelling and meanings of the words. The last exercise page is a word search puzzle with all twenty-five words hidden inside a jumble of letters. Then there is a test page to see how well you have learned.

On the test, you will have to write each of the unit's twenty-five words in the blank next to its meaning. This will test your knowledge of both meanings and spellings. There are also some blanks at the top of each test for review words from previous units. The teacher will read these words out loud, and you will write them down. The purpose of this part of the test is to keep you from forgetting the spelling of words you have already learned. When you study for each week's test, you should also look over the words from previous units, concentrating especially on the words that gave you trouble.

The two-part box at the top of each page is for your grade. The number already filled in is the number of questions on the page, and the empty space is where you or your teacher can write the number you got right on that page. At the back of the book is a progress chart ro record your grades as you go through the units.

If at any point you find the material too hard and you are getting frustrated, be sure to ask for help from your teacher, your friends, or your parents. It is especially important that someone help you study for the tests by reading the words out loud to you and testing you on the spelling and the meanings. Here's a hint for the third and fourth pages in each unit: every time you find a word and write it on a line, cross that word out on the word list at the top of the page. This way the job gets easier and easier as you go along.

If you are finding *Vocabulary—Book 2* too easy, here are some things you can do to challenge yourself and to make the exercises more fun.

1. Look up each word in a dictionary, write out the syllabication and pronunciation marks, and list any extra meanings that don't appear in the book.
2. On the first and second pages of each unit, try to use all twelve or thirteen words in one story that makes sense. You can change the order if you want.
3. On the third and fourth pages of each unit, cover up the word list and try to answer all the questions without looking at the list. Then check your work.
4. On the third and fourth pages, try to think of at least one synonym for each answer and write it down on an extra sheet of paper. Use a dictionary or thesaurus if you need help.

Good luck with this book. If you work carefully and consistently, you should be a better speller and writer by the time you get through.

KIM MARSHALL

Contents

Word List for Book 1 and Book 2

(Number in parentheses refers to the unit in which the word appears)

abandon (1)
accelerator (32)
accept (12)
accent (22)
accidentally (29)
accuse (13)
addict (8)
address (3)
admire (13)
advantage (14)
adventure (9)
advertisement (8)
advice (4)
advise (4)
afford (15)
aisle (28)
alert (5)
alley (27)
alphabet (26)
already (6)
although (16)
amazed (29)
ambulance (23)
amnesia (17)
amphibian (18)
amputate (23)
amusing (33)
ancestor (12)
anchor (25)
ancient (36)
anesthetic (22)
announce (10)
annual (20)
antenna (30)
anxious (23)
apartment (23)
apologize (29)
appendix (20)
appetite (34)
applause (33)
appreciate (9)
aquarium (11)
architect (27)
argument (8)
arrest (5)

arrive (23)
artery (32)
artificial (28)
ashamed (35)
aspirin (12)
assassinate (36)
assembly (21)
astonished (33)
ate (11)
attack (17)
attention (7)
attractive (34)
audience (33)
author (24)
automatic (11)
automobile (32)
autumn (14)
avoid (1)
awkward (24)

bachelor (7)
badge (25)
bakery (31)
balance (8)
balloon (32)
banana (28)
bandage (26)
banister (1)
barbecue (12)
bare (1)
barrel (3)
basketball (29)
battery (13)
bear (1)
beard (14)
beautiful (30)
because (9)
beginning (4)
believe (15)
berry (13)
bicycle (5)
binoculars (19)
birthday (12)
blanket (11)

blew (12)
blister (27)
blizzard (13)
blue (12)
board (23)
boast (2)
boomerang (6)
bored (23)
bother (16)
boulder (29)
bounce (29)
boycott (36)
brake (3)
break (3)
breathe (18)
breakfast (1)
breeze (19)
bridge (10)
bruise (20)
building (23)
burglar (30)
burst (32)
bury (13)
business (30)
busy (32)
butcher (23)

cafeteria (16)
calendar (35)
calf (36)
camel (22)
camera (26)
cancel (35)
cancer (16)
candle (21)
cannibal (35)
canoe (33)
canteen (24)
capital (27)
captain (19)
capture (1)
carpenter (19)
carrot (34)
cartoon (11)

castle (24)
cattle (24)
cautious (11)
ceiling (7)
celebrate (12)
cellar (20)
cement (25)
cemetary (30)
center (31)
century (8)
cereal (1)
certain (28)
challenge (4)
champion (4)
channel (26)
character (11)
chauffeur (36)
cheerful (1)
cheeseburger (2)
chef (34)
chilly (12)
chimney (3)
chocolate (18)
choice (13)
choir (26)
choose (14)
Christmas (16)
church (26)
cigar (3)
cigarette (3)
circle (9)
circus (4)
climate (15)
climax (21)
climb (31)
closet (5)
clumsy (5)
coach (2)
coast (2)
cobra (6)
cockpit (16)
cockroach (29)
coconut (17)
coffee (1)
coffin (30)

collapse (23)
collar (25)
collect (18)
college (19)
comedian (33)
commit suicide (6)
company (10)
compare (20)
compass (25)
complain (16)
compliment (30)
computer (30)
conceal (32)
concentrate (28)
concert (15)
condition (35)
confess (36)
confident (22)
confusing (21)
congratulate (34)
conscience (33)
consider (34)
continent (24)
conversation (6)
convertible (11)
corpse (5)
correct (7)
corridor (25)
cough (31)
counterclockwise (8)
country (23)
courage (12)
court (2)
cousin (1)
coward (12)
crawl (7)
creep (7)
criminal (2)
criticize (12)
crocodile (17)
crowded (3)
cruel (13)
crutch (14)
curious (26)
curtain (9)
curve (4)

daily (9)
damage (36)

dangerous (1)
daughter (15)
debt (5)
deceive (27)
decide (6)
decorate (16)
defeat (29)
deliberately (29)
delicate (17)
delicious (34)
dentist (29)
deny (13)
depth (18)
describe (19)
description (15)
desert (18)
deserted (18)
deserve (18)
design (27)
desperate (8)
despise (10)
dessert (18)
destroy (20)
detective (15)
devour (36)
diamond (30)
diary (9)
dictionary (7)
different (23)
difficult (5)
dinosaur (20)
direction (25)
disagree (8)
disaster (3)
discouraged (35)
discover (33)
disease (16)
disguise (31)
disgusting (36)
dishonest (22)
disobey (21)
distance (33)
distract (7)
disturb (13)
divorce (31)
doctor (23)
dodge (34)
dollar (24)
dolphin (28)
donkey (5)

double-cross (11)
doubt (7)
drenched (25)
drizzle (16)
dwarf (31)
dynamite (28)

earthquake (36)
easily (8)
eavesdrop (6)
echo (23)
eclipse (26)
editor (3)
education (21)
effort (1)
eight (11)
either (12)
election (3)
electrician (13)
electricity (14)
elephant (31)
elevator (23)
embarrassing (9)
emergency (23)
enemy (10)
energy (20)
engine (32)
enormous (19)
enough (4)
entrance (15)
envelope (2)
equator (5)
errand (27)
error (6)
escalator (31)
escape (16)
especially (29)
evening (17)
everybody (18)
everywhere (19)
exaggerate (7)
example (10)
excellent (20)
except (30)
exciting (21)
excuse (32)
execute (35)
exercise (20)
exhausted (20)

expect (36)
expensive (22)
explain (21)
explode (33)
explore (33)
explosion (28)
extinct (20)

factory (18)
faint (31)
faith (34)
false (24)
familiar (11)
famine (9)
famous (32)
fatal (25)
faucet (31)
fault (8)
favorite (28)
feathers (26)
feeble (1)
feint (31)
fierce (12)
filthy (25)
finally (3)
fire hydrant (13)
flatter (13)
flavor (15)
flour (19)
flower (19)
flying saucer (28)
foreign (22)
forward (14)
foul (7)
fountain (9)
fraction (4)
fragile (15)
freeze (11)
french fries (2)
frightened (27)
frisk (27)
funeral (30)
furious (6)
furnace (20)
furniture (16)
further (29)
future (35)

gamble (17)
garage (18)
garbage (18)
gasoline (32)
general (10)
generous (19)
genius (10)
gentle (20)
genuine (24)
ghost (10)
giant (30)
gigantic (7)
giggle (35)
giraffe (36)
glance (22)
glutton (36)
goose (21)
gorgeous (33)
gorilla (1)
gossip (34)
government (4)
graduation (24)
gravity (11)
grease (22)
Greece (22)
greedy (14)
groan (36)
groceries (22)
grouchy (32)
grown (36)
guarantee (25)
guard (2)
guest (31)
guide (8)
guilty (2)
guitar (28)
gymnasium (26)

habit (1)
hamburger (2)
handcuffs (2)
handkerchief (22)
handsome (13)
harbor (19)
haunt (10)
headache (12)
healthy (3)
heard (8)
heart (13)

heaven (14)
heavy (14)
height (9)
herd (8)
heroin (8)
higher (20)
hijack (4)
hinge (15)
hire (20)
history (36)
hoarse (30)
hockey (5)
hole (14)
holiday (27)
hollow (6)
holster (16)
honest (29)
horizon (19)
horrible (3)
horse (30)
hospital (23)
hostage (17)
hungry (22)
hurricane (21)
husband (17)
hypocrite (14)

iceberg (19)
ignorant (18)
I'll (28)
illegal (19)
imagine (10)
imitate (35)
immediately (9)
impatient (8)
important (20)
impossible (30)
improve (32)
including (35)
incredible (7)
information (36)
inherit (36)
injured (21)
innocent (2)
insect (23)
insist (23)
instigator (21)
instinct (33)
instrument (34)

insurance (24)
intelligent (28)
interesting (11)
interrupt (13)
introduce (7)
investigate (15)
invisible (25)
island (25)
ivory (31)

janitor (31)
jealous (8)
jigsaw puzzle (5)
jittery (28)
journey (26)
judge (2)
juice (1)
jury (2)

kangaroo (12)
ketchup (2)
kettle (3)
kitchen (13)
knee (14)
knife (9)

language (22)
laugh (4)
laundry (25)
lawyer (2)
leather (24)
length (26)
lettuce (4)
library (15)
license (32)
lightning (23)
limousine (36)
liquor (5)
listen (6)
lonely (27)
loose (14)
lose (14)
lousy (14)
loyal (6)

machine (16)

magazine (8)
magician (33)
mail (2)
male (2)
manager (29)
maniac (17)
married (17)
mattress (19)
mayor (20)
meant (10)
measure (26)
medicine (23)
memory (20)
mercy (30)
message (1)
messenger (1)
microphone (25)
microscope (33)
midget (32)
millionaire (36)
miniature (32)
minute (35)
miracle (36)
mirror (9)
miser (14)
mistake (22)
mitten (21)
moist (33)
monkey (34)
monster (33)
mosquito (35)
motorcycle (24)
mountain (34)
movie (21)
murder (5)
muscle (11)
museum (7)
mustard (2)
mystery (15)

narrow (24)
necessary (25)
needle (22)
neighbor (31)
neither (8)
nervous (28)
nightmare (11)
noisy (26)
nonsense (1)

notice (12)
nuisance (35)
nurse (23)

obey (10)
object (3)
obvious (13)
ocean (19)
o'clock (14)
octopus (11)
odor (12)
offer (9)
officer (10)
old-fashioned (4)
onion (15)
operator (6)
opinion (15)
optimistic (27)
orchestra (15)
orphan (5)
ounce (27)
overdose (8)
oxygen (6)

package (16)
panic (29)
parachute (17)
parrot (35)
passenger (18)
patient (19)
pause (16)
paws (16)
peace (29)
perfect (10)
perfume (20)
permission (30)
pessimistic (27)
photograph (26)
piano (32)
picnic (22)
picture (10)
piece (29)
pierce (29)
pigeon (35)
pitcher (10)
plain (15)
plane (15)
plunge (36)

plywood (22)
pneumonia (21)
poison (34)
pollution (18)
popular (33)
portable (34)
positive (24)
postpone (35)
pour (11)
practice (7)
praise (25)
precious (30)
predict (35)
prefer (31)
prejudiced (31)
prepare (8)
present (28)
president (27)
pretend (28)
prevent (26)
principal (21)
principle (21)
prison (2)
private (6)
probably (1)
professor (12)
progress (3)
promise (13)
prompt (4)
propeller (17)
protect (5)
protest (27)
puncture (16)
punish (29)

quarrel (17)
quench (18)
question (26)

rabbit (20)
radar (30)
radiator (24)
raisin (11)
rattlesnake (34)
razor (7)
reach (25)
really (31)
reason (28)

receive (26)
recently (1)
recess (12)
recognize (31)
recommend (3)
recover (5)
reflect (27)
refuse (16)
regret (29)
regular (17)
rehearse (10)
relative (20)
relief (30)
reluctant (35)
remember (17)
repair (34)
repeat (24)
reporter (3)
rescue (11)
respect (7)
restaurant (34)
result (25)
revenge (31)
reverse (28)
reward (26)
rhythm (12)
ridiculous (27)
right (5)
ring (25)
riot (6)
roast (35)
robbery (2)
robot (16)
rooster (17)
root (33)
rough (19)
route (33)
rubbish (30)
ruin (35)
rumor (7)

salary (31)
sandwich (22)
sarcastic (26)
satisfied (1)
sauce (12)
sausage (3)
saxophone (13)
scalp (4)

scarce (5)
scared (5)
scene (17)
school (21)
scientist (33)
scissors (27)
scrape (4)
scratch (6)
scream (11)
screwdriver (19)
search (16)
season (14)
secret (6)
secretary (29)
seen (17)
seldom (17)
sensible (18)
sentence (19)
serious (10)
shallow (4)
shampoo (18)
share (20)
shiver (28)
shoulder (30)
shovel (36)
shrink (21)
sieve (17)
sigh (33)
sign (33)
signature (34)
silence (24)
simple (11)
siren (7)
skeleton (25)
skunk (12)
skyscraper (6)
slaughter (31)
sleeve (6)
slippery (8)
smooth (19)
smother (28)
smuggle (8)
sneeze (22)
soar (34)
soldier (10)
sole (6)
somersault (26)
sore (34)
soul (6)
sour (15)

spaghetti (34)
spare (12)
special (3)
speedometer (32)
spinach (17)
splinter (19)
sponge (13)
spread (9)
sprinkle (4)
squeeze (24)
squirm (27)
squirrel (18)
stair (26)
stare (26)
starve (9)
statue (13)
steak (6)
steal (27)
steel (27)
stingy (16)
stomach (29)
straight (17)
strange (28)
strangle (18)
strawberry (3)
stretcher (23)
strict (19)
stumble (24)
style (10)
submarine (17)
suburb (30)
successful (32)
suddenly (35)
suede (36)
suffer (9)
sugar (3)
suggest (22)
sundae (18)
Sunday (18)
supermarket (22)
surgeon (20)
surprise (7)
surrender (10)
surround (21)
survive (34)
suspicious (15)
swallow (24)
sweat (15)
sweater (28)
sweet (15)

switch (22)
sword (21)

tailor (11)
tape recorder (25)
tease (25)
telephone (31)
telescope (8)
television (11)
temperature (32)
tennis (28)
terrible (13)
terrific (26)
terrified (33)
theater (1)
thermometer (32)
thief (12)
thirsty (24)
though (14)
thought (14)
thread (9)
threaten (9)
threw (14)
throat (30)
through (14)
toast (1)
tobacco (3)
together (14)
tomorrow (9)
tongue (4)
toothache (29)
torture (15)
tough (5)
towel (27)
traffic (8)
tragedy (13)
translate (22)
treasure (6)
trial (2)
trouble (16)
trousers (4)
tunnel (7)
turkey (29)
turtle (17)
typewriter (29)

umbrella (16)
umpire (18)

unbelievable (19)
uncomfortable (10)
unconscious (23)
underneath (23)
unexpected (5)
uniform (20)
unusual (21)
usually (21)

vacation (16)
vacuum cleaner (30)
vain (32)
valley (32)
valuable (35)
vanilla (18)
vegetable (36)
vein (32)
verdict (2)
victim (22)
victory (34)
violin (15)
visitor (5)
voice (21)
volcano (33)
vulture (5)

waist (24)
wait (7)
wallet (34)
warn (9)
waste (24)
watch (27)
waterproof (27)
wealthy (24)
weapon (21)
wear (10)
weary (11)
weather (35)
weight (7)
where (10)
whether (35)
which (4)
whirl (25)
whisper (31)
whistle (8)
whole (14)
windshield (32)
witch (4)

witness (2)
wonderful (28)
worn (9)
worried (26)
worst (4)
wound (9)
wreck (9)
wrestle (13)
wring (25)
wrinkled (4)
wrist (6)
write (5)
wrong (3)

yesterday (7)

Read each of the following words and its meaning. Then use each word or set of words in a good sentence.

1. *flower* — the blossom of a plant

_____

2. *flour* — a white powder made from grain, used to make bread, cookies, cake

_____

3. *college* — a two- or four-year school after high school

_____

4. *describe* — to use words to tell about something or someone

_____

5. *generous* — giving freely; not stingy

_____

6. *illegal* — against the law

_____

7. *unbelievable* — too unusual or unlikely to be believed

_____

8. *rough* — uneven; not smooth
   smooth — even; without bumps

_____

9. *splinter* — a small, sharp fragment broken off a piece of wood or glass

_____

10. *carpenter* — a person who builds things with wood
    screwdriver — a tool used to turn screws

_____

11. Which two words are antonyms? _____ _____

12. Which word rhymes with *puff?* _____

Read each of the following words and its meaning. Then use each word or set of words in a good sentence.

1. *mattress* — a large pad filled with springy material (cotton, rubber) which people sleep on

_____

2. *patient* — able to wait calmly, without getting upset; *also* someone under a doctor's care

_____

3. *sentence* — a group of words (containing a subject and a verb) expressing a thought

_____

4. *strict* —following rules very carefully; not letting anyone get away with anything; severe

_____

5. *everywhere* — in each and every place; all around

_____

6. *breeze* — a light wind

_____

7. *harbor* — a sheltered area of water where ships stay to be safe from winds or storms

_____

8. *captain* — the person in charge; the leader (as of a boat, an athletic team)
   ocean — a very large body of salt water (as the Atlantic, Pacific, Indian, Arctic)

_____

9. *iceberg* — a big chunk of floating ice
   enormous — extremely big

_____

10. *binoculars* — a compact double telescope to make distant things look closer
    horizon — the line far away where the sky meets the land (or water)

_____

11. Which word rhymes with *devotion?* _____

12. Which word can also mean a length of time served in jail for a crime? _____

Write each word after its meaning. Choose from the following list.

flower	flour	college	describe	generous
illegal	unbelievable	rough	smooth	splinter
carpenter	screwdriver	mattress	patient	sentence
strict	everywhere	breeze	harbor	captain
ocean	iceberg	enormous	binoculars	horizon

1. a sheltered area of water where ships stay to be safe from winds or storms _____

2. a large pad filled with springy material which people sleep on _____

3. against the law _____

4. a small, sharp fragment broken off a piece of wood or glass _____

5. a tool used to turn screws _____

6. a two- or four-year school after high school _____

7. a light wind _____

8. able to wait calmly, without getting upset _____

9. the person in charge; the leader _____

10. a compact double telescope to make distant things look closer _____

11. to use words to tell about something or someone _____

12. a very large body of salt water _____

13. a white powder made from grain, used to make bread _____

14. a person who builds things with wood _____

15. the line far away where the sky meets the land (or water) _____

16. in each and every place _____

17. a group of words (containing a subject and verb) expressing a thought

_____

18. the blossom of a plant _____

19. too unusual or unlikely to be believed _____

20. even; without bumps _____

21. a big chunk of floating ice _____

22. following rules very carefully; severe _____

23. uneven; not smooth _____

24. giving freely; not stingy _____

25. extremely big _____

Complete the following sentences by filling in the right word. Choose from the list below and use each word only once.

flower	flour	college	describe	generous
illegal	unbelievable	rough	smooth	splinter
carpenter	screwdriver	mattress	patient	sentence
strict	everywhere	breeze	harbor	captain
ocean	iceberg	enormous	binoculars	horizon

1. My sister wants to go to _____ and learn about business.

2. The ship disappeared over the _____, and they never saw it again.

3. He wrote a poem about a lovely _____ he saw one spring day.

4. The man swore loudly when he got the _____ under his fingernail.

5. You might as well be _____; the plane won't come for another hour.

6. She looked _____ and still couldn't find the missing ring.

7. An _____ wave nearly tipped over the ocean liner.

8. It was very _____ of you to buy me this lovely necklace.

9. The sailboat made it into the _____ just as the storm broke.

10. The pancake recipe called for a cup of _____.

11. In South Africa it is_____ for Black people to marry white people.

12. The board was _____ before they sandpapered it.

13. Get the _____ out of the tool box so we can put the hinges on the door.

14. The light _____ wasn't enough to make the sailboat move quickly.

15. The _____ of the gymnastics team won an Olympic medal.

16. They were shipwrecked on a tiny island in the middle of the _____.

17. It's hard for me to _____ the sunset; it was very beautiful.

18. The woman complained that the _____ in the hotel room was lumpy.

19. After my father shaves, his face looks _____ and clean.

20. It may sound _____, but I swear that this story is true.

21. The _____ spent three days building a new bookshelf in the hall.

22. The *Titanic* sank when it struck a large _____.

23. She told the story in one long _____, without taking a breath.

24. They used the _____ to see what kind of geese were flying by.

25. The _____ teacher didn't allow any talking in class.

The twenty-five words you have learned in this unit are hidden in the following puzzle. Circle the words and write them on the lines at the right. The words can be found going across, up and down, and diagonally (/).

```
U  T  B  C  L  J  T  E  C  N  E  T  N  E  S
M  N  Z  S  R  A  L  U  C  O  N  I  B  T  C
E  T  B  S  S  S  H  A  R  B  O  R  R  P  R
V  J  R  E  T  P  Z  X  B  W  X  I  T  S  E
E  L  E  J  L  L  M  K  Z  T  C  B  L  J  W
R  T  E  S  L  I  E  U  I  T  F  E  J  T  D
Y  L  Z  E  U  N  E  B  U  C  L  M  B  T  R
W  Z  E  W  D  T  M  V  O  C  E  A  N  T  I
H  B  T  Z  T  E  S  S  A  A  A  B  X  N  V
E  V  J  V  U  R  J  R  L  B  M  N  O  E  E
R  P  N  I  A  T  P  A  C  Q  L  R  S  I  R
E  T  X  Z  T  E  W  I  S  Z  T  E  S  T  T
B  U  D  D  N  D  C  S  S  E  R  T  T  A  M
M  B  A  T  E  E  I  O  O  H  O  U  J  P  P
D  L  E  M  B  Q  R  B  J  G  T  Z  L  B  D
M  R  Q  E  R  B  J  Z  T  U  L  M  B  T  S
L  Q  R  N  R  B  G  D  H  O  R  I  Z  O  N
J  G  M  O  B  T  E  B  I  R  C  S  E  D  J
R  A  E  R  I  O  N  U  L  E  U  E  G  A  E
E  I  H  M  O  O  E  U  L  E  A  A  E  E  R
W  I  T  O  U  U  R  B  E  J  K  K  L  J  U
O  M  O  U  N  N  O  Q  G  R  A  Z  L  T  O
L  M  O  S  O  J  U  P  A  D  Z  L  O  O  L
F  Q  M  R  B  D  S  C  L  A  D  M  C  O  F
B  U  S  Q  R  B  S  D  Z  L  O  M  Q  R  B
```

1. _____
2. _____
3. _____
4. _____
5. _____
6. _____
7. _____
8. _____
9. _____
10. _____
11. _____
12. _____
13. _____
14. _____
15. _____
16. _____
17. _____
18. _____
19. _____
20. _____
21. _____
22. _____
23. _____
24. _____
25. _____

Write down the review words as they are dictated to you.

1. _____
2. _____
3. _____
4. _____
5. _____
6. _____
7. _____
8. _____
9. _____

Write each of this unit's words on the line after its meaning.

1. extremely big _____

2. a sheltered area of water where ships stay to be safe from winds or storms _____

3. the person in charge; the leader _____

4. a large pad filled with springy material which people sleep on _____

5. able to wait calmly, without getting upset _____

6. against the law _____

7. a light wind _____

8. a small, sharp fragment broken off a piece of wood or glass _____

9. a two- or four-year school after high school _____

10. a tool used to turn screws _____

11. a compact double telescope to make distant things look closer _____

12. a very large body of salt water _____

13. to use words to tell about something or someone _____

14. a white powder made from grain, used to make bread _____

15. a person who builds things with wood _____

16. in each and every place _____

17. the line far away where the sky meets the land (or water) _____

18. a group of words (containing a subject and verb) expressing a thought

_____

19. the blossom of a plant _____

20. even; without bumps _____

21. too unusual or unlikely to be believed _____

22. a big chunk of floating ice _____

23. following rules very carefully; severe _____

24. uneven; not smooth _____

25. giving freely; not stingy _____

Read each of the following words and its meaning. Then use each word or set of words in a good sentence.

1. *higher* — more high; raised up more; the opposite of lower

_____

2. *hire* — to take someone on for a job

_____

3. *annual* — happening once a year

_____

4. *compare* — to examine things to see how they are different and the same

_____

5. *destroy* — to wreck or ruin something

_____

6. *excellent* — extremely good; superb

_____

7. *important* — deserving attention; noteworthy

_____

8. *perfume* — a sweet-smelling liquid that people put on to smell nice

_____

9. *gentle* — treating someone or something nicely, not roughly
   bruise — a tender, often black and blue spot on your skin where something has hit you

_____

10. *surgeon* — a doctor specially trained to operate on people
    appendix — a short, closed tube off the intestine

_____

11. In which word does the *s* have a /z/ sound? _____

12. Which word is an antonym of *build?* _____

Read each of the following words and its meaning. Then use each word or set of words in a good sentence.

1. *rabbit* — a small animal with soft fur and big ears

   _____

2. *relative* — a person in your family; someone related to you by blood

   _____

3. *memory* — the power of remembering

   _____

4. *share* — to give part of what you have to another person (or other people)

   _____

5. *uniform* — clothes specially designed for a group of people (policemen, nurses)

   _____

6. *mayor* — the person elected to be in charge of a city or town

   _____

7. *cellar* — the basement; the part of a building that is underground
   furnace — a machine to heat a building (usually found in the cellar)

   _____

8. *dinosaur* — a kind of reptile that lived on the earth millions of years ago
   extinct — died out; no more left in existence

   _____

9. *exercise* — to work out; to move your body around a lot
   exhausted — very tired out

   _____

10. *energy* — power or strength; the force that makes a person or machine able to perform

   _____

11. Which word rhymes with *player?* _____

12. Which word rhymes with *fair?* _____

13. Which word rhymes with *more?* _____

Write each word after its meaning. Choose from the following list.

higher	hire	annual	compare	destroy
excellent	important	perfume	gentle	bruise
surgeon	appendix	rabbit	relative	memory
share	uniform	mayor	cellar	furnace
dinosaur	extinct	exercise	exhausted	energy

1. clothes specially designed for a group of people _____

2. a small animal with soft fur and big ears _____

3. a machine to heat a building _____

4. power or strength; the force that makes a person or machine able to perform _____

5. to examine things to see how they are different and the same _____

6. a sweet-smelling liquid that people put on to smell nice _____

7. a kind of reptile that lived on the earth millions of years ago _____

8. a person in your family; someone related to you by blood _____

9. to wreck or ruin something _____

10. deserving attention; noteworthy _____

11. a doctor specially trained to operate on people _____

12. the basement; the part of a building that is underground _____

13. more high; raised up more; the opposite of lower _____

14. a short, closed tube off the intestine _____

15. happening once a year _____

16. treating someone or something nicely, not roughly _____

17. to give part of what you have to another person _____

18. to work out; to move your body around a lot _____

19. extremely good; superb _____

20. the power of remembering _____

21. very tired out _____

22. a tender spot on your skin where something has hit you _____

23. to take someone on for a job _____

24. died out; no more left in existence _____

25. the person elected to be in charge of a city or town _____

Complete the following sentences by filling in the right word. Choose from the list below and use each word only once.

higher	hire	annual	compare	destroy
excellent	important	perfume	gentle	bruise
surgeon	appendix	rabbit	relative	memory
share	uniform	mayor	cellar	furnace
dinosaur	extinct	exercise	exhausted	energy

1. Her mother told her to be very _____ with the tiny baby.

2. He has a big, ugly _____ on his leg where the baseball hit him.

3. Why don't you _____ your candy with us, you greedy pig?

4. The _____ escaped the dog by darting under a barbed wire fence.

5. An atomic bomb is powerful enough to _____ an entire city.

6. It is against the law to refuse to _____ someone because of race or color.

7. We could smell her _____ in the room hours after she had left.

8. All of my _____s are coming for Christmas dinner.

9. Whales will become _____ if people don't stop killing them.

10. Many Americans would probably be healthier if they would _____ .

11. She was rushed to the hospital to have her _____ taken out.

12. He had a terrific _____ for people's names; he never forgot one.

13. The _____ broke down, and the whole house was freezing cold.

14. The judge told the jury to listen carefully to this _____ evidence.

15. They had an _____ celebration of the day they were married.

16. It would be amazing to see a _____ walking the earth today.

17. The _____ of their house filled with water during the flood.

18. The baseball team got new doubleknit _____s.

19. She did an _____ job on the painting and won first prize.

20. The pilot said, "If we fly a little _____, we will be above the storm."

21. The girl was completely _____ at the end of the marathon.

22. The _____ decided that the sick man needed a heart transplant.

23. The police officers asked the _____ to pay them higher wages.

24. Human beings get their _____ by burning the calories in food.

25. If you _____ the two poems, you'll see which one is better.

The twenty-five words you have learned in this unit are hidden in the following puzzle. Circle the words and write them on the lines at the right. The words can be found going across, up and down, and diagonally (/).

```
E M D B Z T L J S Q R B C L S     1. _____
M N X I B C J P L S S P R J U     2. _____
U E E F N P J E V I T A L E R     3. _____
R C Q R D O M N J P L X P R G     4. _____
D M B C G E S I C R E X E W E     5. _____
C L J L K Y B A D F W Y L Y O     6. _____
Z R A E X B D C U N U B J T N     7. _____
C A P P E N D I X R Q R B D C     8. _____
L B J D M D E T S U A H X E B     9. _____
L B D C L J B A D H E I O U J    10. _____
E I B D E U J B E R A P M O C    11. _____
C T U T C K T X S B D R M B Y    12. _____
A A B C D G C E T F G H E R I    13. _____
N R A L L E C J R K L M O N O    14. _____
R O O O L N P Q O R S M T U V    15. _____
U V L W T X Y Y Z E J P Z L      16. _____
F T E O O L J D E M U F R E P    17. _____
M N J J P E K U K D E M N O L    18. _____
T A J P C A N E I X O U Y B D    19. _____
R T H D C I M B T D B L M H D    20. _____
C R J B F Z Z I Z R E H G I H    21. _____
P O O O O O N J U B J T Z R T    22. _____
S P R S T C I M A Y O R E J      23. _____
N M O J T P S S S T B L N T M    24. _____
B I L C D E W X C L A U N N A    25. _____
```

Write down the review words as they are dictated to you.

1. _____   4. _____   7. _____

2. _____   5. _____   8. _____

3. _____   6. _____   9. _____

Write each of this unit's words on the line after its meaning.

1. to examine things to see how they are different and the same _____

2. power or strength; the force that makes a person or machine able to perform

   _____

3. a sweet liquid that people put on to smell nice _____

4. a machine to heat a building _____

5. a kind of reptile that lived on the earth millions of years ago _____

6. a small animal with soft fur and big ears _____

7. a person in your family; someone related to you by blood _____

8. clothes specially designed for a group of people _____

9. the basement; the part of a building that is underground _____

10. to wreck or ruin something _____

11. more high; raised up more; the opposite of lower _____

12. deserving attention; noteworthy _____

13. to give part of what you have to another person _____

14. a doctor specially trained to operate on people _____

15. to work out; to move your body around a lot _____

16. a short, closed tube off the intestine _____

17. extremely good; superb _____

18. happening once a year _____

19. the power of remembering _____

20. treating someone or something nicely; not roughly _____

21. the person elected to be in charge of a city or town _____

22. very tired out _____

23. died out; no more left in existence _____

24. a tender spot on your skin where something has hit you _____

25. to take someone on for a job _____

Read each of the following words and its meaning. Then use each word or set of words in a good sentence.

1. *principle* — a rule that a person believes in and acts on

   _____

2. *principal* — the person in charge of a school
   disobey — to go against orders

   _____

3. *school* — a place of teaching and learning
   education — knowledge and learning gained from study or experiences

   _____

4. *assembly* — a group gathered together for a common purpose

   _____

5. *explain* — to make something easy to understand; to give the reasons for

   _____

6. *candle* — a wax stick used to produce light by burning the wick in the middle

   _____

7. *confusing* — unclear; tending to mix you up

   _____

8. *voice* — the sound made by your lungs and throat

   _____

9. *shrink* — to become smaller or less

   _____

10. *pneumonia* — a disease of the lungs

   _____

11. Which words are homonyms? _____   _____

12. Which word rhymes with *yule?* _____

Read each of the following words and its meaning. Then use each word or set of words in a good sentence.

1. *goose* — a water bird with a long neck (in the same family as ducks)

   _____

2. *usually* — normally; happens most of the time

   _____

3. *unusual* — not happening very often; strange; out of the ordinary

   _____

4. *instigator* — someone who stirs up fights between other people

   _____

5. *mitten* — a covering for the hand with one place for the thumb and another for the four fingers

   _____

6. *surround* — to be on all sides; all around

   _____

7. *movie* — a motion picture; a film

   _____

8. *exciting* — causing strong feelings; making people get worked up
   climax — the most exciting part of a story or movie

   _____

9. *sword* — an old-fashioned weapon with a long, sharp, metal blade
   weapon — an instrument used for fighting

   _____

10. *injured* — hurt; wounded
    hurricane — a very serious storm with winds over seventy-five miles an hour

    _____

11. Which word rhymes with *groovy?* _____

12. Which word rhymes with *reward?* _____

13. Which word is usually found in pairs? _____

Write each word after its meaning. Choose from the following list.

principle	principal	disobey	school	education
assembly	explain	candle	confusing	voice
shrink	pneumonia	goose	usually	unusual
instigator	mitten	surround	movie	climax
exciting	sword	weapon	injured	hurricane

1. a covering for the hand with one place for the thumb and another for the four fingers

   _____

2. a water bird with a long neck (in the same family as ducks) _____

3. the person in charge of a school _____

4. to make something easy to understand; to give the reasons for _____

5. a disease of the lungs _____

6. a place of teaching and learning _____

7. the most exciting part of a story or movie _____

8. a very serious storm with winds over seventy-five miles an hour _____

9. to be on all sides; all around _____

10. normally; happens most of the time _____

11. to go against orders _____

12. unclear; tending to mix you up _____

13. to become smaller or less _____

14. hurt; wounded _____

15. someone who stirs up fights between other people _____

16. a rule that a person believes in and acts on _____

17. an old-fashioned weapon with a long, sharp metal blade _____

18. not happening very often; strange; out of the ordinary _____

19. knowledge and learning gained from study or experiences _____

20. the sound made by your lungs and throat _____

21. causing strong feelings; making people get worked up _____

22. a wax stick used to produce light by burning it _____

23. a motion picture; a film _____

24. an instrument used for fighting _____

25. a group gathered together for a common purpose _____

Complete the following sentences by filling in the right word. Choose from the list below and use each word only once.

principle	principal	disobey	school	education
assembly	explain	candle	confusing	voice
shrink	pneumonia	goose	usually	unusual
instigator	mitten	surround	movie	climax
exciting	sword	weapon	injured	hurricane

1. *The Wizard of Oz* was her favorite _____.

2. When the electricity went out, they hunted for a _____.

3. Luckily she was not _____ when she slipped on the ice.

4. At the city park we saw a lone _____ paddling on the edge of the pond.

5. "If you _____ my orders, you'll be punished," said the general.

6. Non-violence was a very important _____ to Martin Luther King, Jr.

7. It would be quite _____ to have a snowstorm in July.

8. I tried to _____ the algebra to her, but she didn't understand.

9. It is true that with an _____ you can usually get a better job.

10. That wool sweater will _____ if you put it in the hot wash water.

11. The _____ lifted the roof right off their house.

12. At the _____ of the movie, the man escaped from jail and was free.

13. That workbook is very _____ because there are no directions.

14. My mother was afraid I had _____, but it was only a bad cold.

15. I _____ go to bed at 10:30 P.M.

16. The new school _____ is much more popular than the old one.

17. It must have been so _____ to be the first person on the moon!

18. When I heard her _____ on the telephone, it sounded familiar.

19. The English soldier drew his _____ and prepared for the duel.

20. Every student in the school went to the _____ to hear the speaker.

21. That _____ managed to stir up a fight between the two boys.

22. She lost one _____, so her hand got very cold.

23. A karate expert knows how to use the hand as a deadly _____.

24. He always regretted dropping out of _____.

25. The movie star could hardly move because she was _____ed by so many fans.

The twenty-five words you have learned in this unit are hidden in the following puzzle. Circle the words and write them on the lines at the right. The words can be found going across, up and down, and diagonally (/).

V	O	O	R	B	J	T	U	N	I	A	L	P	X	E	1. _____
J	P	K	H	I	J	P	L	D	M	C	Q	U	P	C	2. _____
K	S	R	M	B	D	M	C	Q	R	B	D	R	V	L	3. _____
D	C	M	I	I	J	Y	E	B	O	S	I	D	O	Q	4. _____
E	H	O	O	N	T	D	P	S	L	N	M	C	I	C	5. _____
R	O	L	J	Q	C	T	H	H	C	I	L	B	C	Y	6. _____
U	O	L	Q	A	D	I	E	I	M	I	B	R	E	L	7. _____
J	L	C	N	B	L	O	P	N	M	R	K	C	J	L	8. _____
N	P	D	D	R	B	L	C	A	X	B	N	W	Y	A	9. _____
I	L	O	R	H	E	B	X	D	L	M	I	Y	Z	U	10. _____
E	P	O	A	C	E	D	B	U	V	W	R	X	Y	S	11. _____
B	R	E	C	L	M	B	U	R	O	D	H	L	M	U	12. _____
G	N	I	S	U	F	N	O	C	F	E	S	O	O	G	13. _____
B	D	V	W	L	O	R	U	B	A	D	Q	R	B	C	14. _____
I	D	O	O	M	X	N	C	S	Q	T	R	O	M	L	15. _____
N	G	M	R	R	U	S	S	P	L	O	I	B	D	N	16. _____
S	M	B	D	S	C	E	Q	R	B	D	J	O	M	O	17. _____
T	Q	F	U	U	M	A	I	N	O	M	U	E	N	P	18. _____
I	B	A	D	B	S	U	R	R	O	U	N	D	S	A	19. _____
G	L	H	L	I	R	T	B	L	Q	R	M	D	P	E	20. _____
A	J	Y	M	B	D	L	O	R	C	P	L	M	N	W	21. _____
T	D	M	P	E	N	A	C	I	R	R	U	H	R	W	22. _____
O	P	R	D	Z	M	X	P	Z	L	M	Q	R	B	W	23. _____
R	C	C	L	O	H	I	Z	P	J	M	P	B	L	I	24. _____
W	R	B	L	R	Z	M	G	N	I	T	I	C	X	E	25. _____

Write down the review words as they are dictated to you.

1. _____   4. _____   7. _____

2. _____   5. _____   8. _____

3. _____   6. _____   9. _____

Write each of this unit's words on the line after its meaning.

1. a group gathered together for a common purpose _____

2. an instrument used for fighting _____

3. a motion picture; a film _____

4. a wax stick used to produce light by burning it _____

5. causing strong feelings; making people get worked up _____

6. the sound made by your lungs and throat _____

7. knowledge and learning gained from study or experiences _____

8. not happening very often; strange; out of the ordinary _____

9. an old-fashioned weapon with a long, sharp, metal blade _____

10. a rule that a person believes in and acts on _____

11. someone who stirs up fights between other people _____

12. hurt; wounded _____

13. to become smaller or less _____

14. unclear; tending to mix you up _____

15. to go against orders _____

16. normally; happens most of the time _____

17. to be on all sides; all around _____

18. a very serious storm with winds over seventy-five miles an hour _____

19. the most exciting part of a story or movie _____

20. a place of teaching and learning _____

21. a disease of the lungs _____

22. to make something easy to understand; to give the reasons for _____

23. the person in charge of a school _____

24. a water bird with a long neck (in the same family as ducks) _____

25. a covering for the hand with one place for the thumb and another for the four fingers

_____

Read each of the following words and its meaning. Then use each word or set of words in a good sentence.

1. *grease* — fat used for cooking; *also* a heavy substance used to oil an engine

   _____

2. *Greece* — a country in eastern Europe on the Mediterranean Sea.

   _____

3. *switch* — a small lever which turns things on and off

   _____

4. *camel* — a desert animal with a hump on its back

   _____

5. *confident* — sure of oneself

   _____

6. *dishonest* — can't be trusted; not honest

   _____

7. *glance* — a quick look

   _____

8. *supermarket* — a big store which sells all kinds of foods and supplies
   groceries — foods and supplies for the kitchen

   _____

9. *expensive* — costing a lot of money

   _____

10. *handkerchief* — a piece of cloth used to blow the nose or cry into
    sneeze — to breathe out suddenly because of a tickling feeling in your nose

    _____

11. Which word is an antonym of *cheap?* _____

12. Which word is an antonym of *nervous?* _____

13. Which three words have a *c* with an /s/ sound?

    _____   _____   _____

Read each of the following words and its meaning. Then use each word or set of words in a good sentence.

1. *hungry* — wanting something to eat

_____

2. *suggest* — to present an idea for people to think about

_____

3. *picnic* — an outing where food is brought along and eaten outside

_____

4. *sandwich* — two slices of bread with food between them

_____

5. *plywood* — very strong wood made of several layers of wood glued together

_____

6. *victim* — the injured person, especially in an accident or crime

_____

7. *mistake* — an error; something done wrong

_____

8. *translate* — to change words from one language into another
   language — the words used by a specific group of people to speak and write

_____

9. *accent* — the way people pronounce words (gives you a clue about where they come from)
   foreign — from another country

_____

10. *needle* — a small, sharp, pointed piece of metal or plastic (used in sewing or for shots)
    anesthetic — a substance used to stop pain during an operation (in the form of a shot or gas)

_____

11. Which word breaks the rule "*i* before *e* except after *c*"? _____

12. In which two words does a *g* have a /j/ sound? _____ _____

Write each word after its meaning. Choose from the following list.

grease	Greece	switch	camel	confident
dishonest	glance	supermarket	groceries	expensive
handkerchief	sneeze	hungry	suggest	picnic
sandwich	plywood	victim	mistake	translate
language	accent	foreign	needle	anesthetic

1. two slices of bread with food between them _____

2. wanting something to eat _____

3. a small, sharp, pointed piece of metal or plastic _____

4. costing a lot of money _____

5. sure of oneself _____

6. a desert animal with a hump on its back _____

7. a country in eastern Europe on the Mediterranean Sea _____

8. a piece of cloth used to blow the nose or cry into _____

9. the injured person, especially in an accident or crime _____

10. an outing where food is brought along and eaten outside _____

11. a substance used to stop pain during an operation _____

12. a small lever which turns things on and off _____

13. a quick look _____

14. to change words from one language into another _____

15. fat used for cooking; *also* a heavy substance used to oil an engine _____

16. can't be trusted; not honest _____

17. an error; something done wrong _____

18. to breathe out suddenly because of a tickling feeling in your nose _____

19. the way people pronounce words _____

20. a big store which sells all kinds of foods and supplies _____

21. very strong wood made of several layers of wood glued together _____

22. from another country _____

23. foods and supplies for the kitchen _____

24. to present an idea for people to think about _____

25. the words used by a specific group of people to speak and write _____

Complete the following sentences by filling in the right word. Choose from the list below and use each word only once.

grease	Greece	switch	camel	confident
dishonest	glance	supermarket	groceries	expensive
handkerchief	sneeze	hungry	suggest	picnic
sandwich	plywood	victim	mistake	translate
language	accent	foreign	needle	anesthetic

1. The _____ walked across the desert for five days without water.

2. You could tell by his _____ that he came from the South.

3. They gave her an _____ and then began the operation.

4. Some people think that _____ cars are better than American cars.

5. They went to the nearby market and spent sixty dollars on _____.

6. "I'm so _____ I could eat a horse!" she said.

7. He was optimistic about the game; he was _____ they could win it.

8. The mechanic came home with _____ all over his clothes.

9. The _____ was closed, and there was nowhere else to buy food.

10. English is the international _____ of the sea.

11. When he had his cold, he was using up a _____ an hour.

12. The woman's job was to _____ the Russian book into English.

13. We built a strong bookshelf out of bricks and _____.

14. "Please _____ at this report before I send it on," she said to her assistant.

15. The quarterback made a bad _____ trying to pass on the fourth down.

16. The Rolls-Royce is one of the most _____ cars in the world.

17. They flew to _____ and spent their first night in Athens.

18. She winced when the doctor stuck the _____ into her arm.

19. He was the only _____ of armed robbery in the city all year.

20. Their _____ was ruined by a heavy rainstorm.

21. People who testify in court must take an oath not to be _____.

22. He put ham, American cheese, lettuce, and tomatoes in the _____.

23. My sudden _____ blew the papers right off the desk.

24. She groped around trying to find the light _____ in the dark room.

25. "What do you _____ I do about my bad breath?" she asked.

The twenty-five words you have learned in this unit are hidden in the following puzzle. Circle the words and write them on the lines at the right. The words can be found going across, up and down, and diagonally (/).

```
C H R L B J S B L F E R O D P     1. _____
J A Q A E T A L S N A R T O C     2. _____
D N M N V B J Q O C P S S B D     3. _____
L D R G I B Q R C O D O C L J     4. _____
P K J U S R R E P I C N I C T     5. _____
S E X A N W N C S D M B Q E R     6. _____
C R M G E T E H F I J H K X Y     7. _____
Z C P E P O O P U V W R H I C     8. _____
J H P D X N M E B Q A R E L T     9. _____
M I T Z E L J S P M L J K P N    10. _____
D E M S Q R E A R D L J A T E    11. _____
S F T U N L V E H C K H T I D    12. _____
J P C L D E P R P U L B S T I    13. _____
S L M E X U E G B T N E I Z F    14. _____
P J E N S X R Z Z V T G M L N    15. _____
H N M B G E T Z E L I J R A O    16. _____
C T B R E I B C Q R B C D Y C    17. _____
I M B C T X E S X W Z T T S B    18. _____
W H E I R J T R S H R D P I B    19. _____
D L M E J E P R O H C B T L M    20. _____
N Z P P C T Z L S F C T M B H    21. _____
A U J N H D O O W Y L P I S B    22. _____
S A A S U G G E S T S T L W B    23. _____
T L M B J S E I R E C O R G S    24. _____
G R B C I T E H T S E N A Z A    25. _____
```

Write down the review words as they are dictated to you.

1. _____   4. _____   7. _____

2. _____   5. _____   8. _____

3. _____   6. _____   9. _____

Write each of this unit's words on the line after its meaning.

1. an outing where food is brought along and eaten outside _____

2. the injured person, especially in an accident or crime _____

3. a piece of cloth used to blow the nose or cry into _____

4. a country in Eastern Europe on the Mediterranean Sea _____

5. a desert animal with a hump on its back _____

6. sure of oneself _____

7. costing a lot of money _____

8. a small, sharp, pointed piece of metal or plastic _____

9. wanting something to eat _____

10. two slices of bread with food between them _____

11. the words used by a specific group of people to speak and write _____

12. to present an idea for people to think about _____

13. foods and supplies for the kitchen _____

14. from another country _____

15. very strong wood made of several layers of wood glued together _____

16. a big store which sells all kinds of foods and supplies _____

17. the way people pronounce words _____

18. to breathe out suddenly because of a tickling feeling in your nose _____

19. an error; something done wrong _____

20. can't be trusted; not honest _____

21. fat used for cooking; *also* a heavy substance used to oil an engine _____

22. to change words from one language into another _____

23. a quick look _____

24. a small lever which turns things on and off _____

25. a substance used to stop pain during an operation _____

Read each of the following words and its meaning. Then use each word or set of words in a good sentence.

1. *board* — a flat piece of wood

_____

2. *bored* — not at all interested in something

_____

3. *arrive* — to reach the place where you were going

_____

4. *butcher* — a person who cuts and sells meat

_____

5. *insect* — a small animal like an ant, fly, or spider

_____

6. *country* — a nation; *also* an area away from cities

_____

7. *lightning* — the flashing of light caused by bolts of electricity in the sky

_____

8. *insist* — not to give way on something you are asking for; to keep asking or demanding

_____

9. *emergency* — a bad situation that has to be taken care of right away
   hospital — a place that takes care of sick and injured people

_____

10. *medicine* — a drug used for treating a sickness
    nurse — a person trained to help take care of sick people

_____

11. Which word has four syllables? _____

12. In which two words does the *c* have an /s/ sound? _____ _____

Read each of the following words and its meaning. Then use each word or set of words in a good sentence.

1. *different* — not the same; dissimilar

   _____

2. *echo* — a sound bouncing back at you

   _____

3. *underneath* — under or below something; beneath

   _____

4. *apartment* — one or more rooms serving as a home in a larger building

   _____

5. *elevator* — a small compartment that takes people up and down inside buildings

   _____

6. *collapse* — to cave in; to fall down
   building — a structure (such as a house, school, or office) with walls and a roof

   _____

7. *unconscious* — knocked out; not awake

   _____

8. *anxious* — worried

   _____

9. *stretcher* — a light, bedlike arrangement for carrying a sick or wounded person
   ambulance — a special vehicle for carrying sick or injured people

   _____

10. *doctor* — a person trained and licensed to heal sick or injured people
    amputate — to cut off part of the body because it is infected or injured

   _____

11. In which word does *ch* have a /k/ sound? _____

12. Which word begins with *a* and has two syllables? _____

Write each word after its meaning. Choose from the following list.

board	bored	arrive	butcher	insect
country	lightning	insist	emergency	hospital
medicine	nurse	different	echo	underneath
apartment	elevator	collapse	building	unconscious
anxious	stretcher	ambulance	doctor	amputate

1. a small compartment that takes people up and down inside buildings _____

2. worried _____

3. a special vehicle for carrying sick or injured people _____

4. a nation; *also* an area away from cities _____

5. to reach the place where you were going _____

6. a flat piece of wood _____

7. a light, bedlike arrangement for carrying a sick or wounded person _____

8. one or more rooms serving as a home in a larger building _____

9. a person who cuts and sells meat _____

10. not to give way on something you are asking for _____

11. a drug used for treating a sickness _____

12. not at all interested in something _____

13. to cave in; to fall down _____

14. a sound bouncing back at you _____

15. to cut off part of the body because it is infected or injured _____

16. under or below something; beneath _____

17. the flashing of light caused by bolts of electricity in the sky _____

18. a place that takes care of sick and injured people _____

19. a structure with walls and a roof _____

20. a person trained to help take care of sick people _____

21. a small animal like an ant, fly, or spider _____

22. knocked out; not awake _____

23. a bad situation that has to be taken care of right away _____

24. not the same; dissimilar _____

25. a person trained and licensed to heal sick or injured people _____

Complete the following sentences by filling in the right word. Choose from the list below and use each word only once.

board	bored	arrive	butcher	insect
country	lightning	insist	emergency	hospital
medicine	nurse	different	echo	underneath
apartment	elevator	collapse	building	unconscious
anxious	stretcher	ambulance	doctor	amputate

1. The _____ struck the tree and split it in half.

2. The children decided to find out what was _____ the house.

3. They carried the injured football player off the field on a _____.

4. The woman went to her _____ to ask about her frequent headaches.

5. The _____ sold them a beautiful steak for the birthday party.

6. His leg was so badly injured that they had to _____.

7. The heavy rain softened the earth and made the tunnel _____.

8. The girl got so _____ with the class that she fell asleep.

9. Every person in the world has _____ fingerprints.

10. He was very _____ to hear the results of the difficult exam.

11. Their _____ had three bedrooms, a living room, and a kitchen.

12. The _____ took them up to the sixtieth floor in no time.

13. The _____ is fun to visit, but I'd rather live in the city.

14. They fixed up the old, deserted _____ so that it could be used for housing.

15. The doctor gave him gas to make him _____ during the operation.

16. "This is an _____!" she shouted. "Call the police at once!"

17. I feel fine, but if you _____, I will go see a doctor.

18. The black belt karate expert could break a thick _____ with his hand.

19. The _____ got her ready for the operation.

20. He spent all afternoon waiting for his father's train to _____.

21. She could hear the _____ of her voice across the valley.

22. The doctor prescribed a new _____ to cure her dizziness.

23. The _____ raced through the streets with its light flashing.

24. She left the _____ three days after the operation.

25. He noticed a tiny _____ crawling along the chair.

The twenty-five words you have learned in this unit are hidden in the following puzzle. Circle the words and write them on the lines at the right. The words can be found going across, up and down, and diagonally (/).

```
G T O S U O I C S N O C N U N
B A Z D M G N I N T H G I L U
X Y R B Z T W X Y U V W N U R
B B J R E N I C I D E M S D S
Z U L V I N S E C T U V I J E
H C T B I V U J E A F G S H P
R O O C H J E B N Q O P T J C
R L S P H R D X C Q D R A O B
M L D P A E I V U J D P U S O
B A Q O I O R O J I M N P U R
Z P Z T U T U Q F R T O A N E
T S M S B D A F Q R R P B D D
L E L Q O O E L Y U A V B E J
G O E P B R D M Q R R D B R D
R L T F E C H O T D P O B N O
E R A N B C L M J M B C D E O
H R T B C C E G Y H F T E A O
C J U M M N P C N D C O A T U
T V P V T J N X W I X R C H L
E M M M J E P Z X V D U V W X
R M A Q G U V C D A U L P I F
T J M R P L O R R R S P I J M
S B E L E V A T O R J Q R U D
L M M J P R O D L C Q R B D B
E M D L Q R E C N A L U B M A
```

1. _____
2. _____
3. _____
4. _____
5. _____
6. _____
7. _____
8. _____
9. _____
10. _____
11. _____
12. _____
13. _____
14. _____
15. _____
16. _____
17. _____
18. _____
19. _____
20. _____
21. _____
22. _____
23. _____
24. _____
25. _____

Write down the review words as they are dictated to you.

1. _____ 4. _____ 7. _____

2. _____ 5. _____ 8. _____

3. _____ 6. _____ 9. _____

Write each of this unit's words on the line after its meaning.

1. a small compartment that takes people up and down inside buildings _____

2. to reach the place where you were going _____

3. worried _____

4. a flat piece of wood _____

5. a special vehicle for carrying sick or injured people _____

6. a light, bedlike arrangement for carrying a sick or wounded person _____

7. a nation; *also* an area away from cities _____

8. one or more rooms serving as a home in a larger building _____

9. a person who cuts and sells meat _____

10. to cave in; to fall down _____

11. not to give way on something you are asking for _____

12. a sound bouncing back at you _____

13. a drug used for treating a sickness _____

14. to cut off part of the body because it is infected or injured _____

15. not at all interested in something _____

16. under or below something; beneath _____

17. the flashing of light caused by bolts of electricity in the sky _____

18. a small animal like an ant, fly, or spider _____

19. a structure with walls and a roof _____

20. knocked out; not awake _____

21. a place that takes care of sick and injured people _____

22. a bad situation that has to be taken care of right away _____

23. a person trained to help take care of sick people _____

24. a person trained and licensed to heal sick or injured people _____

25. not the same; dissimilar _____

Read each of the following words and its meaning. Then use each word or set of words in a good sentence.

1. *waist* — the middle of your body; where a belt is often worn

_____

2. *waste* — to use a lot when you need only a little

_____

3. *author* — the writer of a book or article

_____

4. *continent* — one of the seven large bodies of land in the world (such as North America, Europe, and Asia)

_____

5. *false* — untrue; not the real thing; fake

_____

6. *wealthy* — rich

_____

7. *awkward* — clumsy; without grace
   stumble — to trip over something

_____

8. *castle* — a large house or fort built in the old days, usually made to protect the people inside

_____

9. *cattle* — cows, bulls, or oxen

_____

10. *leather* — animal skin that can be made into shoes, coats, wallets
    genuine — the real thing; sincere

_____

11. Which two words are antonyms? _____ _____

12. Which word rhymes with *hassle?* _____

Read each of the following words and its meaning. Then use each word or set of words in a good sentence.

1. *motorcycle* — a two-wheeled vehicle run by a motor

_____

2. *radiator* — a metal device for heating a room (using steam, electricity, or water)

_____

3. *repeat* — to do or say again

_____

4. *silence* — without noise; stillness; quiet

_____

5. *swallow* — to move something from your mouth down your throat

_____

6. *insurance* — an agreement in which a company promises, in return for a certain amount of money, to pay a person in case of loss or injury

_____

7. *graduation* — the successful completion of the necessary grades and courses of a school

_____

8. *positive* — sure; certain; no chance of a mistake (Are you *positive* that's the man?)
   dollar — one hundred cents in American or Canadian money

_____

9. *narrow* — not wide; hard to fit through or into
   squeeze — to push in the sides of something and make it smaller

_____

10. *canteen* — a small bottle (made of metal, plastic) for carrying water or other liquids
    thirsty — wanting something to drink

_____

11. In which word does *c* have one /s/ and one /k/ sound? _____

12. Which word rhymes with *holler?* _____

Write each word after its meaning. Choose from the following list.

waist   waste   author   continent   false
wealthy   awkward   stumble   castle   cattle
leather   genuine   motorcycle   radiator   repeat
silence   swallow   insurance   graduation   positive
dollar   narrow   squeeze   canteen   thirsty

1. a metal device for heating a room _____

2. sure; certain; no chance of a mistake _____

3. wanting something to drink _____

4. untrue; not the real thing; fake _____

5. cows, bulls, or oxen _____

6. the real thing; sincere _____

7. the middle of your body; where a belt is often worn _____

8. clumsy; without grace _____

9. to push in the sides of something and make it smaller _____

10. to move something from your mouth down your throat _____

11. not wide; hard to fit through or into _____

12. a large house or fort built in the old days _____

13. to use a lot when you need only a little _____

14. rich _____

15. the successful completion of the necessary grades and courses of a school _____

16. to do or say again _____

17. a two-wheeled vehicle run by a motor _____

18. one of the seven large bodies of land in the world _____

19. to trip over something _____

20. a small bottle for carrying water or other liquids _____

21. without noise; stillness; quiet _____

22. the writer of a book or article _____

23. animal skin that can be made into shoes, coats, wallets _____

24. an agreement in which a company promises to pay a person in case of loss or injury

_____

25. one hundred cents in American or Canadian money _____

Complete the following sentences by filling in the right word. Choose from the list below and use each word only once.

waist	waste	author	continent	false
wealthy	awkward	stumble	castle	cattle
leather	genuine	motorcycle	radiator	repeat
silence	swallow	insurance	graduation	positive
dollar	narrow	squeeze	canteen	thirsty

1. The tunnel was too _____ for the big man to crawl through.

2. The family got an _____ payment for their stolen camera.

3. He left the _____ bill in his pants when they were washed, and he got back laundered money.

4. Australia is the smallest _____ in the world.

5. The _____ was proud to see her book on sale in the bookstore.

6. It is dangerous not to wear a helmet while riding a _____.

7. Finally the _____ heated up, and the room became cozy again.

8. She was _____, but the water in the river was too dirty to drink.

9. The cowboy rode all over looking for his herd of stolen _____.

10. ''Are you _____ you had your wallet with you?'' she asked.

11. He took too big a bite of the sandwich and couldn't _____ it.

12. She likes to _____ a person's hand firmly when she shakes hands.

13. The spy gave the people at the airport a _____ name.

14. The king took refuge inside his _____ during the revolution.

15. It's a _____ of electricity to leave lights on all night.

16. The boxer danced around his opponent and made him look _____.

17. Her entire family came to her _____ from college.

18. The man turned up his hearing aid and asked her to _____ the story.

19. After the awful news was announced, there was _____ in the room.

20. His _____ had become larger, and the pants were too tight for him.

21. She told him that the coat was _____ leather.

22. They became a very _____ family after oil was discovered on their land.

23. The smiling circus clown pretended to _____ over his own feet.

24. The coat looked like _____, but it was really plastic.

25. Make sure you have enough water in your _____ for the hike.

The twenty-five words you have learned in this unit are hidden in the following puzzle. Circle the words and write them on the lines at the right. The words can be found going across, up and down, and diagonally (/).

```
G  B  H  R  W  K  O  B  W  O  L  L  A  W  S      1. _____
L  H  M  B  Z  T  W  U  S  V  A  W  E  C  D      2. _____
M  B  V  H  D  M  C  Q  T  L  K  J  T  A  M      3. _____
B  E  V  D  L  U  U  N  C  W  K  F  B  N  L      4. _____
J  V  T  S  B  E  E  E  A  R  T  I  H  T  B      5. _____
M  I  J  M  E  N  K  R  N  Z  W  L  J  E  T      6. _____
O  T  M  Z  I  B  D  D  L  I  M  Z  T  E  T      7. _____
T  I  E  T  S  S  B  R  L  E  U  A  T  N  A      8. _____
O  S  N  R  J  T  O  S  L  D  E  N  L  U  V      9. _____
R  O  L  W  T  H  L  B  S  P  M  V  E  B  P     10. _____
C  P  L  A  T  Y  M  E  E  R  B  L  A  G  T     11. _____
Y  W  L  U  J  U  T  R  M  B  T  T  T  L  Z     12. _____
C  T  A  J  T  T  S  B  A  T  R  A  H  B  T     13. _____
L  R  S  S  S  S  S  A  D  T  R  E  A  B       14. _____
E  L  E  L  T  S  A  C  M  J  I  K  R  H  I     15. _____
I  R  B  S  W  E  A  L  T  H  Y  A  F  E  N     16. _____
F  N  I  B  J  D  M  Q  R  B  D  V  T  W  S     17. _____
X  A  Y  B  R  A  R  A  L  L  O  D  D  O  U     18. _____
W  R  L  R  B  Z  T  L  J  T  M  Z  D  M  R     19. _____
S  R  S  S  I  L  E  N  C  E  R  D  M  I  A     20. _____
H  O  B  E  E  D  U  V  D  W  Z  L  Y  D  N     21. _____
R  W  S  S  N  O  I  T  A  U  D  A  R  G  C     22. _____
M  Q  R  D  C  L  M  J  T  C  L  R  M  B  E     23. _____
D  L  M  X  B  X  W  Y  T  S  R  I  H  T  Y     24. _____
V  B  T  L  A  R  D  M  L  R  Q  R  D  S  S     25. _____
```

Write down the review words as they are dictated to you.

1. _____   4. _____   7. _____

2. _____   5. _____   8. _____

3. _____   6. _____   9. _____

Write each of this unit's words on the line after its meaning.

1. one hundred cents in American or Canadian money _____

2. an agreement in which a company promises to pay a person in case of loss or injury

   _____

3. animal skin that can be made into shoes, coats, wallets _____

4. the writer of a book or article _____

5. without noise; stillness; quiet _____

6. a small bottle for carrying water or other liquids _____

7. to trip over something _____

8. one of the seven large bodies of land in the world _____

9. a two-wheeled vehicle run by a motor _____

10. to do or say again _____

11. the successful completion of the necessary grades and courses of a school _____

12. rich _____

13. to use a lot when you need only a little _____

14. a large house or fort built in the old days _____

15. not wide; hard to fit through or into _____

16. to move something from your mouth down your throat _____

17. to push in the sides of something and make it smaller _____

18. clumsy; without grace _____

19. the middle of your body; where a belt is often worn _____

20. the real thing; sincere _____

21. cows, bulls, or oxen _____

22. untrue; not the real thing; fake _____

23. wanting something to drink _____

24. sure; certain; no chance of a mistake _____

25. a metal device for heating a room _____

Read each of the following words and its meaning. Then use each word or set of words in a good sentence.

1. *ring* — the sound made by a bell

_____

2. *wring* — to twist and squeeze, usually to get water out of something
laundry — clothes and other things that need to be washed or have been washed

_____

3. *collar* — the part of a shirt, coat, or dress that goes around the neck
filthy — very dirty

_____

4. *badge* — a special sign or button worn to show that a person belongs to a certain group

_____

5. *cement* — a common building material (clay and limestone mixed with sand and water)

_____

6. *corridor* — a hall, usually with doors opening into it

_____

7. *drenched* — soaking wet

_____

8. *fatal* — enough to kill; lethal

_____

9. *guarantee* — to promise; especially to promise in writing that a product will work right and last a certain length of time

_____

10. *invisible* — not able to be seen by the human eye

_____

11. In which word does the *g* have a /j/ sound? _____

12. Which word is an antonym of *spotless?* _____

13. Which word is an antonym of *parched?* _____

Read each of the following words and its meaning. Then use each word or set of words in a good sentence.

1. *reach* — to arrive at; to be able to touch

_____

2. *result* — the end product; occurring because of some cause

_____

3. *praise* — to say nice things about a person

_____

4. *skeleton* — the structure of bones of a person or animal

_____

5. *tease* — to make fun of; to kid

_____

6. *necessary* — needing to be done; essential

_____

7. *whirl* — to spin around very fast

_____

8. *tape recorder* — a machine to record sounds on tape
   microphone — a device to pick up sounds for a tape recorder or loudspeaker

_____

9. *compass* — an instrument for figuring out direction using a magnetic needle that points north
   direction — the way something is pointed or moving (north, south, east, or west)

_____

10. *anchor* — a heavy object on a rope which is thrown overboard to keep a boat from drifting
    island — a small body of land completely surrounded by water

_____

11. In which three words does the *s* have a /z/ sound?

_____   _____   _____

12. Which word rhymes with *furl?* _____

13. Which word rhymes with *banker?* _____

Write each word after its meaning. Choose from the following list.

ring	wring	laundry	collar	filthy
badge	cement	corridor	drenched	fatal
guarantee	invisible	reach	result	praise
skeleton	tease	necessary	whirl	microphone
tape recorder	compass	direction	anchor	island

1. needing to be done; essential _____

2. to arrive at; to be able to touch _____

3. a heavy object on a rope used to keep a boat from drifting _____

4. a common building material _____

5. to twist and squeeze, usually to get water out of something _____

6. to promise, especially to promise in writing _____

7. soaking wet _____

8. to spin around very fast _____

9. to say nice things about a person _____

10. a small body of land completely surrounded by water _____

11. the structure of bones of a person or animal _____

12. a special sign or button worn to show that a person belongs to a certain group _____

13. clothes and other things that need to be washed _____

14. not able to be seen by the human eye _____

15. a device to pick up sounds for a tape recorder or loudspeaker _____

16. the end product; occurring because of some cause _____

17. the way something is pointed or moving _____

18. very dirty _____

19. enough to kill; lethal _____

20. the part of a shirt, coat, or dress that goes around the neck _____

21. the sound made by a bell _____

22. to make fun of; to kid _____

23. a machine to record sounds on tape _____

24. a hall, usually with doors opening into it _____

25. an instrument for figuring out direction _____

Complete the following sentences by filling in the right word. Choose from the list below and use each word only once.

ring	wring	laundry	collar	filthy
badge	cement	corridor	drenched	fatal
guarantee	invisible	reach	result	praise
skeleton	tease	necessary	whirl	microphone
tape recorder	compass	direction	anchor	island

1. The radio came with a year's _____ that it wouldn't break down.

2. Her umbrella broke, and she was _____ in the thunderstorm.

3. She jumped up as soon as she heard the telephone _____.

4. After the muddy football game, his pants were _____.

5. He said he didn't think they could _____ New York before nightfall.

6. The mad scientist invented a drug that would make her _____.

7. The F.B.I. agent showed them his _____ and then arrested them.

8. Luckily, the baby had not swallowed a _____ dose of the ant poison.

9. The teacher would always _____ people for good work.

10. The _____ broke, and they couldn't find their way out of the woods.

11. The workers poured the _____ foundations for the new building.

12. The business executive wore a white shirt with a button-down _____.

13. They waited around until midnight to hear the _____ of the game.

14. The reporter used a hidden _____ to pick up the conversation.

15. She liked to _____ around until she was very dizzy.

16. My sister gets upset if we _____ her about being fat.

17. It turned quite warm, and the heavy jacket he brought along wasn't _____.

18. Her footsteps echoed down the long, empty _____.

19. They were told to _____ out the clothes and hang them up to dry.

20. The ship sailed into the safe harbor and dropped its _____.

21. He asked the forest ranger which _____ was north.

22. My brother does his _____ only once a month.

23. While digging the foundation hole for the building, they found the _____ of a dinosaur.

24. They recorded the play on a _____ and listened to it later.

25. She dreamed of going to live on a small _____ all by herself.

The twenty-five words you have learned in this unit are hidden in the following puzzle. Circle the words and write them on the lines at the right. The words can be found going across, up and down, and diagonally (/).

```
L  R  M  B  L  N  O  T  E  L  E  K  S  C  D      1. _____
A  O  U  R  L  B  Z  T  M  D  Z  L  O  O  T      2. _____
U  R  Z  T  L  O  D  M  C  P  L  L  G  T  E      3. _____
N  R  B  L  Q  R  Z  T  L  R  L  G  M  R  A      4. _____
D  Z  L  N  E  C  E  S  S  A  R  Y  G  T  S      5. _____
R  S  S  B  L  I  T  C  R  I  R  B  L  J  E      6. _____
Y  Z  M  W  B  R  A  E  H  S  I  O  U  R  L      7. _____
B  P  D  B  I  L  H  C  A  E  R  I  E  L  J      8. _____
T  M  D  C  S  L  M  D  Z  E  T  D  M  R  D      9. _____
A  U  E  I  I  C  B  L  S  J  R  T  S  S  B     10. _____
P  D  L  J  V  T  Z  U  L  O  M  J  P  D  F     11. _____
A  E  E  E  N  E  L  J  C  B  B  B  L  I  M     12. _____
Z  N  N  O  I  T  C  E  R  I  D  W  L  U  G     13. _____
Z  O  L  M  J  K  R  H  I  E  L  T  G  G  N     14. _____
T  H  L  M  D  E  R  H  H  H  U  N  R  I        15. _____
D  P  P  Z  P  A  L  C  O  Y  A  Q  I  R  R     16. _____
S  O  S  A  B  L  N  R  O  R  B  Z  R  D  M     17. _____
F  R  T  Q  B  E  L  C  A  M  C  M  W  D  O     18. _____
A  C  O  R  R  T  T  N  H  L  P  Z  B  N  M     19. _____
T  I  R  D  L  G  T  T  O  C  A  L  A  M        20. _____
A  M  K  H  I  E  J  B  N  Z  R  U  S  L  N     21. _____
L  L  L  E  R  R  B  E  T  S  L  A  S  E        22. _____
F  E  E  W  H  I  R  L  M  R  D  M  L  I  O     23. _____
R  B  C  L  J  B  M  O  E  A  G  N  A  C  U     24. _____
R  M  L  A  U  C  D  J  C  M  E  G  D  A  B     25. _____
```

41

Write down the review words as they are dictated to you.

1. _____   4. _____   7. _____

2. _____   5. _____   8. _____

3. _____   6. _____   9. _____

Write each of this unit's words on the line after its meaning.

1. very dirty _____

2. an instrument for figuring out direction _____

3. the way something is pointed or moving _____

4. a hall, usually with doors opening into it _____

5. the end product; occurring because of some cause _____

6. a machine to record sounds on tape _____

7. a device to pick up sounds for a tape recorder or loudspeaker _____

8. to make fun of; to kid _____

9. not able to be seen by the human eye _____

10. the sound made by a bell _____

11. clothes and other things that need to be washed _____

12. the part of a shirt, coat, or dress that goes around the neck _____

13. a special sign or button worn to show that a person belongs to a certain group _____

14. enough to kill; lethal _____

15. the structure of bones of a person or animal _____

16. a small body of land completely surrounded by water _____

17. to twist and squeeze, usually to get water out of something _____

18. to say nice things about a person _____

19. a common building material _____

20. to spin around very fast _____

21. a heavy object on a rope used to keep a boat from drifting _____

22. soaking wet _____

23. to arrive at; to be able to touch _____

24. to promise, especially to promise in writing _____

25. needing to be done; essential _____

Read each of the following words and its meaning. Then use each word or set of words in a good sentence.

1. *stair* — a step (one of a flight of stairs)

_____

2. *stare* — to look at someone or something long and hard

_____

3. *channel* — one station on television or radio; *also* a deep place where boats can move through a harbor

_____

4. *alphabet* — the twenty-six letters we use to form words

_____

5. *eclipse* — the blocking by one heavenly body of the light from another (such as the blocking of the sun's light by the moon)

_____

6. *feathers* — long, light growths that cover birds

_____

7. *gymnasium* — a large room used for indoor sports

_____

8. *noisy* — loud; making lots of sound

_____

9. *curious* — wanting to investigate and learn
   question — what you ask when you don't know something and want an answer

_____

10. *length* — how long something is
    measure — to determine the amount, length, or size of something

_____

11. Which two words have three syllables? _____ _____

12. Which two words rhyme with *bear?* _____ _____

Read each of the following words and its meaning. Then use each word or set of words in a good sentence.

1. *bandage* — white tape or cloth used to cover a cut or other injury

_____

2. *journey* — a long trip

_____

3. *prevent* — to keep something from happening

_____

4. *worried* — concerned; thinking something may go wrong

_____

5. *terrific* — great; very good

_____

6. *somersault* — a leap or roll in which a person turns or flips over completely

_____

7. *sarcastic* — making sharp and cutting comments, often by saying one thing when you mean the opposite

_____

8. *camera* — a device for taking pictures
   photograph — a picture taken by a camera

_____

9. *choir* — a group of singers (especially in a church)
   church — a building where people worship God

_____

10. *reward* — money (or something else of value) given in return for doing something good
    receive — to get; to take in

_____

11. Which word rhymes with *tire?* _____

12. Which word rhymes with *birch?* _____

13. In which word does the *c* have an /s/ sound? _____

Write each word after its meaning. Choose from the following list.

stair	stare	channel	alphabet	eclipse
feathers	gymnasium	noisy	curious	question
length	measure	bandage	journey	prevent
worried	terrific	somersault	sarcastic	camera
photograph	choir	church	reward	receive

1. concerned; thinking something may go wrong _____

2. white tape or cloth used to cover a cut or other injury _____

3. a device for taking pictures _____

4. to get; to take in _____

5. a leap or roll in which a person flips over completely _____

6. a large room used for indoor sports _____

7. to look at someone or something long and hard _____

8. how long something is _____

9. loud; making lots of sound _____

10. a building where people worship God _____

11. great; very good _____

12. to keep something from happening _____

13. money given in return for doing something good _____

14. long, light growths that cover birds _____

15. to determine the amount, length, or size of something _____

16. a long trip _____

17. what you ask when you don't know something and want an answer _____

18. a step _____

19. one station on televison or radio _____

20. a picture taken by a camera _____

21. making sharp and cutting comments _____

22. a group of singers (especially in a church) _____

23. wanting to investigate and learn _____

24. the twenty-six letters we use to form words _____

25. the blocking by one heavenly body of the light from another _____

Complete the following sentences by filling in the right word. Choose from the list below and use each word only once.

stair	stare	channel	alphabet	eclipse
feathers	gymnasium	noisy	curious	question
length	measure	bandage	journey	prevent
worried	terrific	somersault	sarcastic	camera
photograph	choir	church	reward	receive

1. The _____ was closed, so they couldn't play basketball.

2. The room was so _____ that no one could do any homework.

3. One hundred yards is the standard _____ of a football field.

4. The nurse put a _____ on the cut and told him to take it easy.

5. The _____ sang so beautifully that it brought tears to her eyes.

6. The sheriff offered a large _____ for the outlaw's capture.

7. The student's _____ was too hard for the professor to answer.

8. It took them several days to pack for their long _____.

9. The _____ was filled with worshipers on Easter Sunday.

10. Peacocks are known for their brilliant blue and green _____.

11. She wanted to _____ herself to see how much she had grown in a year.

12. He thought she was being _____ when she said he was handsome.

13. In the old days people were terrified of an _____ of the sun.

14. The _____s are very slippery; be careful not to fall.

15. She was so _____ about it that she couldn't stop asking questions.

16. He asked her to take a _____ of him with the fish he had caught.

17. "Did you _____ my letter?" she asked.

18. He knew all the letters of the _____ when he was four years old.

19. The clown did so many _____s that he was too dizzy to stand up.

20. "There's no need to be _____," he said. "She'll get home safely."

21. The police officer took out his _____ to take pictures of the suspect.

22. She looked so different with her hair cut short that all he could do was _____ at her.

23. He asked his brother what _____ the late movie was on.

24. "That was a _____ game!" she said. "Let's play it again."

25. I wish I could _____ her from going on that dangerous rock climbing trip.

The twenty-five words you have learned in this unit are hidden in the following puzzle. Circle the words and write them on the lines at the right. The words can be found going across, up and down, and diagonally (/).

```
A L M P A L C I T S A C R A S    1. _____
L L M E R R Y D M B L J T T Z    2. _____
T D P M P Z W S R E H T A E F    3. _____
E V L H M B R C Q R B I Z L M    4. _____
R R C Q A T N E V E R P M B V    5. _____
R R D C L B M M B R D M L C M    6. _____
I B H T G N E L V H D L O D R    7. _____
F B L G T C A T C Z L M R A E    8. _____
I H J R L L S R B N B Q M N S    9. _____
C Q C I B C U R I O U S B T C    10. _____
M I P O J H R B R E D M A L R    11. _____
Z S M H C B E V S L D R N R R    12. _____
E B V C C D M T L M E Z D W E    13. _____
R O O O D M I L L E N N A H C    14. _____
N F D U R O C U M K C D G R E    15. _____
J O U R N E Y A D R A W E R I    16. _____
M B I V D M W S C R M D L R V    17. _____
U J B S L M D R W V E U N L E    18. _____
I O B I Y A B E A E R R U N V    19. _____
S B V B L P D M R E A H I H J    20. _____
A R D E I R R O W N B R B R D    21. _____
N C M B Z W V S R S S B D A C    22. _____
M L Q R B Z L M B V J T Z M B    23. _____
Y J T S H P A R G O T O H P L    24. _____
G M T H E E N D R B J M D L Q    25. _____
```

Write down the review words as they are dictated to you.

1. _____   4. _____   7. _____

2. _____   5. _____   8. _____

3. _____   6. _____   9. _____

Write each of this unit's words on the line after its meaning.

1. the blocking by one heavenly body of the light from another _____

2. to determine the amount, length, or size of something _____

3. the twenty-six letters we use to form words _____

4. long, light growths that cover birds _____

5. wanting to investigate and learn _____

6. money given in return for doing something good _____

7. a group of singers (especially in a church) _____

8. to keep something from happening _____

9. making sharp and cutting comments _____

10. great; very good _____

11. a picture taken by a camera _____

12. a building where people worship God _____

13. one station on television or radio _____

14. loud; making lots of sound _____

15. a step _____

16. how long something is _____

17. what you ask when you don't know something and want an answer _____

18. to look at someone or something long and hard _____

19. a long trip _____

20. a device for taking pictures _____

21. a large room used for indoor sports _____

22. white tape or cloth used to cover a cut or other injury _____

23. a leap or roll in which a person flips over completely _____

24. concerned; thinking something may go wrong _____

25. to get; to take in _____

Read each of the following words and its meaning. Then use each word or set of words in a good sentence.

1. *steal* — to take something that doesn't belong to you

_____

2. *steel* — a very strong metal used to make cars, bridges, machines

_____

3. *blister* — a swelling on your skin filled with fluid, often caused by rubbing too much against something

_____

4. *deceive* — to trick; to mislead

_____

5. *frisk* —to search a person by patting his or her clothing all over (usually in search of weapons)

_____

6. *squirm* — to twist and turn around; to wriggle

_____

7. *towel* — a cloth for wiping or drying

_____

8. *protest* — to show that you have strong objections to something

_____

9. *architect* — a person who draws the plans to show how a building will be constructed
design — to plan (usually on paper) the way something will be

_____

10. *watch* — a timepiece worn on your wrist
waterproof — not letting water leak in

_____

11. Which word rhymes with *worm?* _____

12. Which word follows the rule "*i* before *e* except after *c*"? _____

Read each of the following words and its meaning. Then use each word or set of words in a good sentence.

1. *ridiculous* — foolish; very silly

_____

2. *scissors* — a cutting instrument made of two sharp blades screwed together

_____

3. *errand* — a short trip to buy or get something

_____

4. *ounce* — a unit of weight (there are sixteen in a pound)

_____

5. *reflect* — to bounce back the image of a picture (as a mirror or other shiny surface does)

_____

6. *optimistic* — looking on the bright side; thinking things will turn out well

_____

7. *pessimistic* — looking on the bad side; thinking things will turn out poorly

_____

8. *holiday* — a vacation; a time when there is no work or school
   lonely — sad from being alone

_____

9. *frightened* — scared, afraid
   alley — a very narrow street between buildings

_____

10. *president* — the person elected to be in charge of a group such as a class, club, or country
    capital — a city where the seat of state or national government is located

_____

11. Which two words are antonyms? _____ _____

12. Which word has a silent *c?* _____

Write each word after its meaning. Choose from the following list.

steal	steel	blister	deceive	frisk
squirm	towel	protest	architect	design
watch	waterproof	ridiculous	scissors	errand
ounce	reflect	optimistic	pessimistic	holiday
lonely	frightened	alley	president	capital

1. a short trip to buy or get something _____

2. to search a person by patting his or her clothing all over _____

3. to show that you have strong objections to something _____

4. scared; afraid _____

5. a city where the seat of state or national government is located _____

6. to twist and turn around; to wriggle _____

7. to trick; to mislead _____

8. to take something that doesn't belong to you _____

9. foolish; very silly _____

10. to bounce back the image of a picture _____

11. a very strong metal used to make cars, bridges, machines _____

12. the person elected to be in charge of a group _____

13. a cloth for wiping or drying _____

14. not letting water leak in _____

15. looking on the bright side; thinking things will turn out well _____

16. a cutting instrument made of two sharp blades screwed together _____

17. a timepiece worn on your wrist _____

18. a vacation; a time when there is no work or school _____

19. a person who draws the plans to show how a building will be constructed

_____

20. looking on the bad side; thinking things will turn out poorly _____

21. a unit of weight (there are sixteen in a pound) _____

22. sad from being alone _____

23. a very narrow street between buildings _____

24. to plan (usually on paper) the way something will be _____

25. a swelling on your skin filled with fluid _____

Complete the following sentences by filling in the right word. Choose from the list below and use each word only once.

steal	steel	blister	deceive	frisk
squirm	towel	protest	architect	design
watch	waterproof	ridiculous	scissors	errand
ounce	reflect	optimistic	pessimistic	holiday
lonely	frightened	alley	president	capital

1. The _____ was blamed for the poor construction of the building.

2. Her mother sent her on an _____ to the supermarket.

3. The _____ of the United States lives in the White House.

4. Thanksgiving Day is a _____ in both the United States and Canada.

5. Be careful not to cut yourself with those sharp _____.

6. The forest ranger got very _____ up on the mountain by himself.

7. It might not be safe to walk down a dark _____ at night.

8. The people marched to the governor's office to _____ the decision to shut down the hospital.

9. That boy was arrested for possession of one _____ of marijuana.

10. "You won't _____ me with that made-up story," said his father.

11. Use this mirror to _____ the sun and attract their attention.

12. Running in the new shoes gave him a bad _____ on his heel.

13. The bullets bounced off the _____ sides of the tank.

14. Madrid is the _____ city of Spain.

15. It took years for people to _____ the first big ocean liners.

16. A person can't hold his breath for twenty minutes; that's _____!

17. I'm pretty _____ about the game; I don't see how we can win.

18. The loud explosion _____ the guard.

19. The raincoat was _____, but he got soaked anyway.

20. The police stopped the men to _____ them for weapons.

21. The wrestler had to _____ frantically to get out of the hold.

22. She thought her interview went well and was _____ about getting the job.

23. He checked the time on his _____ and then started to run.

24. The family was so poor that they had to _____ food to survive.

25. The new _____ got pretty dirty when we used it to dry off the dog.

The twenty-five words you have learned in this unit are hidden in the following puzzle. Circle the words and write them on the lines at the right. The words can be found going across, up and down, and diagonally (/).

C	B	C	Y	A	D	I	L	O	H	D	D	L	F	M	1. _____
A	L	L	E	Y	D	N	A	R	R	E	B	R	R	D	2. _____
R	J	P	J	R	S	T	U	M	N	S	B	J	I	Y	3. _____
C	T	C	B	J	M	R	H	E	O	I	D	A	S	L	4. _____
H	C	Q	R	B	E	C	T	M	B	G	R	P	K	E	5. _____
I	Q	R	B	F	F	H	E	S	D	N	L	E	S	N	6. _____
T	T	L	L	M	G	L	R	J	L	A	E	T	S	O	7. _____
E	K	E	C	I	B	O	L	J	T	G	O	T	Q	L	8. _____
C	C	L	R	E	S	U	N	I	P	W	J	B	U	D	9. _____
T	C	F	B	S	L	J	P	P	E	C	Q	R	I	P	10. _____
P	L	J	I	P	R	A	B	L	J	E	D	C	R	P	11. _____
E	J	C	E	S	C	U	S	S	C	A	V	O	M	R	12. _____
S	S	E	S	F	B	D	M	N	C	Q	T	R	D	E	13. _____
S	U	J	O	P	O	L	U	F	U	E	D	D	P	S	14. _____
I	O	R	P	B	T	O	J	P	S	J	T	C	M	I	15. _____
M	L	B	T	E	B	T	R	T	S	S	P	L	I	D	16. _____
I	U	M	I	C	P	Q	R	P	B	J	T	S	U	E	17. _____
S	C	R	M	B	D	J	R	P	R	C	M	N	H	N	18. _____
T	I	O	I	R	B	E	D	M	E	E	C	S	C	T	19. _____
I	D	T	S	J	T	P	C	L	M	D	T	J	T	Q	20. _____
C	I	R	T	S	C	M	B	E	J	D	M	A	A	Q	21. _____
R	R	X	I	W	C	Y	Z	P	I	L	W	X	W	T	22. _____
L	J	L	C	C	P	Y	A	Z	T	V	S	D	L	J	23. _____
T	B	B	J	K	D	M	B	J	L	E	E	T	S	T	24. _____
C	B	J	M	B	J	D	B	D	M	Q	R	B	T	O	25. _____

Test 27

Write down the review words as they are dictated to you.

1. _____ 4. _____ 7. _____

2. _____ 5. _____ 8. _____

3. _____ 6. _____ 9. _____

Write each of this unit's words on the line after its meaning.

1. to take something that doesn't belong to you _____

2. a short trip to buy or get something _____

3. foolish; very silly _____

4. to search a person by patting his or her clothing all over _____

5. to bounce back the image of a picture _____

6. to show that you have strong objections to something _____

7. a very strong metal used to make cars, bridges, machines _____

8. scared; afraid _____

9. the person elected to be in charge of a group _____

10. a city where the seat of state or national government is located _____

11. a vacation; a time when there is no work or school _____

12. to twist and turn around; to wriggle _____

13. a person who draws the plans to show how a building will be constructed

_____

14. to trick; to mislead _____

15. looking on the bad side; thinking things will turn out poorly _____

16. a cloth for wiping or drying _____

17. a unit of weight (there are sixteen in a pound) _____

18. not letting water leak in _____

19. sad from being alone _____

20. looking on the bright side; thinking things will turn out well _____

21. a very narrow street between buildings _____

22. a cutting instrument made of two sharp blades screwed together _____

23. a swelling on your skin filled with fluid _____

24. a timepiece worn on your wrist _____

25. to plan (usually on paper) the way something will be _____

Read each of the following words and its meaning. Then use each word or set of words in a good sentence.

1. *I'll* — short for *I will*

_____

2. *aisle* — a path where people can walk (as in a church or theater), usually between rows of seats

_____

3. *banana* — a curved, yellow fruit shaped like the new moon

_____

4. *artificial* — made by people; not natural

_____

5. *favorite* — the one you like best of all

_____

6. *certain* — sure; no mistake about it

_____

7. *flying saucer* — a spaceship shaped like a plate or a frisbee

_____

8. *strange* — out of the ordinary; unusual

_____

9. *sweater* — a knitted piece of clothing one wears to keep warm
   shiver — to shake with cold or excitement; to tremble

_____

10. *explosion* — a violent, noisy burst of heat and gas when something blows up
    dynamite — a powerful explosive made into sticks with a fuse

_____

11. In which two words does the *c* have an /s/ sound? _____   _____

12. Which two words rhyme with *mile?* _____   _____

Read each of the following words and its meaning. Then use each word or set of words in a good sentence.

1. *jittery* — shaky, usually due to nervousness

   _____

2. *nervous* — worried; concerned about something

   _____

3. *guitar* — a musical instrument with six or twelve strings played with the fingers

   _____

4. *pretend* — to make believe

   _____

5. *reason* — the cause; why something happened

   _____

6. *reverse* — backward; the opposite of forward

   _____

7. *smother* — to keep someone or something from getting enough air

   _____

8. *tennis* — a sport using rackets, played on a court with a net in the middle
   concentrate — to fix your attention on one thing and not think of other things

   _____

9. *present* — a gift
   wonderful — terrific; really nice

   _____

10. *dolphin* — a porpoise· a kind of water-dwelling mammal
    intelligent — smart; clever

    _____

11. In which two words does the *s* have a /z/ sound? _____ _____

12. Which two words are almost synonyms (mean the same)? _____ _____

Write each word after its meaning. Choose from the following list.

I'll	aisle	banana	artificial	favorite
certain	flying saucer	strange	sweater	shiver
explosion	dynamite	jittery	nervous	guitar
pretend	reason	reverse	smother	tennis
concentrate	present	wonderful	dolphin	intelligent

1. a musical instrument with six or twelve strings played with the fingers _____

2. shaky, usually due to nervousness _____

3. a gift _____

4. smart; clever _____

5. the one you like best of all _____

6. a curved, yellow fruit shaped like the new moon _____

7. to shake with cold or excitement; to tremble _____

8. a powerful explosive made into sticks with a fuse _____

9. short for *I will* _____

10. sure; no mistake about it _____

11. terrific; really nice _____

12. the cause; why something happened _____

13. worried; concerned about something _____

14. a path where people can walk, usually between rows of seats _____

15. a knitted piece of clothing one wears to keep warm _____

16. a violent, noisy burst of heat and gas when something blows up _____

17. a porpoise; a kind of water-dwelling mammal _____

18. to keep someone or something from getting enough air _____

19. to make believe _____

20. made by people; not natural _____

21. out of the ordinary; unusual _____

22. to fix your attention on one thing and not think of other things _____

23. backward; the opposite of forward _____

24. a sport using rackets, played on a court with a net in the middle _____

25. a spaceship shaped like a plate or a frisbee _____

Complete the following sentences by filling in the right word. Choose from the list below and use each word only once.

I'll	aisle	banana	artificial	favorite
certain	flying saucer	strange	sweater	shiver
explosion	dynamite	jittery	nervous	guitar
pretend	reason	reverse	smother	tennis
concentrate	present	wonderful	dolphin	intelligent

1. His mother gave him a bicycle as a birthday _____.

2. The main instrument in the rock band was an electric _____.

3. He lit the fuse of the _____ and ran for cover.

4. She put the car in _____ and backed out of the garage.

5. The _____ I'm all wet is that it's pouring outside.

6. The trainers in the aquarium taught the _____ how to do tricks.

7. We all began to _____ in the cold night air.

8. The thought of the math test the next morning made her feel _____.

9. She was so _____ that her shaking hands spilled coffee all over the table.

10. The bomb's _____ broke windows five miles away.

11. She peeled the _____ and found it was rotten inside.

12. "What is your _____ kind of ice cream?" asked the waitress.

13. The two men claimed they had seen a _____ from Mars.

14. The sixth grader was _____ enough to do high-school work.

15. Since he knew about the party, he had to _____ to be surprised.

16. She could not _____ on her work because of all the noise outside.

17. "I think _____ go for a walk," she announced.

18. He tried to _____ the flames by throwing a blanket on the fire.

19. Isn't it _____ that we have tickets to the world series!

20. We played _____ until our hands were blistered.

21. The theater was too hot, so he took off his _____.

22. He walked down the _____ and onto the stage to receive the prize.

23. "Are you _____ that's the right answer?" she asked.

24. He made the mistake of trying to eat our _____ fruit.

25. The detective thought there was something _____ about the butler.

The twenty-five words you have learned in this unit are hidden in the following puzzle. Circle the words and write them on the lines at the right. The words can be found going across, up and down, and diagonally (/).

```
B J F R D L M H T R A T I U G
P I Z L D M Q B L E P D H B H
N T N U Y U L M N O N O N V S
D T W W C I Z M D I O N U V H
L E Q C O M N D L R A C I Q I
C R B D M N U G N O O T G S V
O Y T U C K D E S B D L R O E
N R B D Z L L E T A O O B E R
C Z W V U Z A U R I U R U S C
E M D O L P H I N F M C S B S
N D M C Q R T S C B U A E D M
T C A R B E D L C I S L N R R
R S M O T H E R B W F D M Y R
A I S L E B D M E C Q I B L D
T L D M T N E G I L L E T N I
E L E S R E V E R R B A B R R
U R R B E N N G N M U N G T A
A E I E T I R O V A F U B Y Z
W D D M A R B T I D N C L M B
R N B R E N N S S S M A S B R
U E V R W E C L G S O G N Q B
R T B N S U O V R E N L C A L
G E T E Z M E R B A W A P Y B
R R R R S T R A N G E Z Z X X
B P H I B Z L G N O S A E R E
```

1. _____
2. _____
3. _____
4. _____
5. _____
6. _____
7. _____
8. _____
9. _____
10. _____
11. _____
12. _____
13. _____
14. _____
15. _____
16. _____
17. _____
18. _____
19. _____
20. _____
21. _____
22. _____
23. _____
24. _____
25. _____

Test 28

Write down the review words as they are dictated to you.

1. _____   4. _____   7. _____

2. _____   5. _____   8. _____

3. _____   6. _____   9. _____

Write each of this unit's words on the line after its meaning.

1. to shake with cold or excitement; to tremble _____

2. a musical instrument with six or twelve strings played with the fingers _____

3. a powerful explosive made into sticks with a fuse _____

4. shaky, usually due to nervousness _____

5. short for *I will* _____

6. a gift _____

7. sure; no mistake about it _____

8. smart; clever _____

9. terrific; really nice _____

10. the one you like best of all _____

11. a violent, noisy burst of heat and gas when something blows up _____

12. a curved, yellow fruit shaped like the new moon _____

13. a porpoise; a kind of water-dwelling mammal _____

14. the cause; why something happened _____

15. to keep someone or something from getting enough air _____

16. worried; concerned about something _____

17. to make believe _____

18. a path where people can walk, usually between rows of seats _____

19. made by people; not natural _____

20. a knitted piece of clothing one wears to keep warm _____

21. backward; the opposite of forward _____

22. out of the ordinary; unusual _____

23. a sport using rackets, played on a court with a net in the middle _____

24. to fix your attention on one thing and not think of other things _____

25. a spaceship shaped like a plate or a frisbee _____

Read each of the following words and its meaning. Then use each word or set of words in a good sentence.

1. *peace* — a state of calm, without war or fighting

_____

2. *piece* — a part of a whole thing
   turkey — a large bird often eaten by people on Thanksgiving

_____

3. *stomach* — the place in the belly where food goes after it is swallowed

_____

4. *pierce* — to make a hole; to stab with a sharp object

_____

5. *amazed* — very surprised

_____

6. *boulder* — a very big rock

_____

7. *cockroach* —an insect that is sometimes found in wet, warm places in homes and other buildings

_____

8. *bounce* — to jump back after hitting something; to rebound

_____

9. *especially* — particularly; more so than others

_____

10. *toothache* — pain in a tooth
    dentist — a person trained to fix and take care of people's teeth

_____

11. In which two words does the *ch* have a /k/ sound? _____ _____

12. Which two words are homonyms? _____ _____

Read each of the following words and its meaning. Then use each word or set of words in a good sentence.

1. *further* — more distant; more far away (in time or space)

_____

2. *honest* — truthful; not lying or cheating

_____

3. *manager* — the person who runs things; the one in charge (of a restaurant, store, theater)

_____

4. *panic* — to become suddenly very frightened by something

_____

5. *punish* — to make someone suffer as a penalty for doing something wrong

_____

6. *secretary* — a person who types and takes care of paperwork for someone
   typewriter — a machine that writes in print when you press its keys

_____

7. *defeat* — to beat someone in a fight or competition
   basketball — a team game played by trying to get a large ball through a hoop

_____

8. *regret* — to feel sorry about something you did

_____

9. *apologize* — to say you are sorry
   accidentally — by mistake; not on purpose

_____

10. *deliberately* — done on purpose

_____

11. In which two words does the *g* have a /j/ sound? _____ _____

12. Which two words are antonyms? _____ _____

Write each word after its meaning. Choose from the following list.

pierce	peace	piece	turkey	stomach
amazed	boulder	cockroach	bounce	especially
toothache	dentist	further	honest	manager
panic	punish	secretary	typewriter	defeat
basketball	regret	apologize	accidentally	deliberately

1. a person who types and takes care of paperwork for someone _____

2. truthful; not lying or cheating _____

3. a state of calm; without war or fighting _____

4. an insect that is sometimes found in wet, warm places in homes and other buildings

_____

5. done on purpose _____

6. pain in a tooth _____

7. a very big rock _____

8. to make a hole; to stab with a sharp object _____

9. particularly; more so than others _____

10. to make someone suffer as a penalty for doing something wrong _____

11. to say you are sorry _____

12. to jump back after hitting something; to rebound _____

13. very surprised _____

14. to become suddenly very frightened by something _____

15. by mistake; not on purpose _____

16. the place in the belly where food goes after it is swallowed _____

17. to feel sorry about something you did _____

18. a large bird often eaten by people on Thanksgiving _____

19. a machine that writes in print when you press its keys _____

20. more distant; more far away _____

21. a person trained to fix and take care of people's teeth _____

22. a part of a whole thing _____

23. a team game played by trying to get a large ball through a hoop _____

24. the person who runs things; the one in charge _____

25. to beat someone in a fight or competition _____

Complete the following sentences by filling in the right word. Choose from the list below and use each word only once.

pierce	peace	piece	turkey	stomach
amazed	boulder	cockroach	bounce	especially
toothache	dentist	further	honest	manager
panic	punish	secretary	typewriter	defeat
basketball	regret	apologize	accidentally	deliberately

1. The team scored no points and suffered a terrible _____.

2. Her _____ ached after she ate two large servings of ice cream.

3. She told her _____ to write a letter arranging a meeting.

4. Now be _____ with me; did you take it or didn't you?

5. He was terrified that the _____ would have to drill his teeth.

6. The people from Mars were _____ at the pollution on Earth.

7. The fire made people in the theater _____, and they trampled each other.

8. The pressure in the bottle made the cork fly up and _____ off the ceiling.

9. After years of war, there was finally _____ in the little town.

10. I _____ that remark I made about your mother; I feel bad about it.

11. She complained to the _____ of the restaurant about the bad meat.

12. The man jumped when he saw the _____ run across the kitchen floor.

13. His mother decided to _____ him for coming home so late.

14. They had an enormous, juicy _____ for Thanksgiving dinner.

15. I think you bumped into me _____; that was no accident.

16. She decided to _____ her ears so she could wear the new earrings.

17. The two-ton _____ rolled down the hill and into the valley.

18. He was _____ careful not to drop the cake he had baked.

19. Didn't you get a _____ of the cake? I'm sorry I forgot you.

20. The electric _____ was useless during the power blackout.

21. I had to _____ to our neighbor for stepping on her flowers.

22. The _____ they went up the mountain, the colder it got.

23. The only cure for the _____ was to remove the tooth.

24. He _____ let the secret slip out.

25. The _____ swished through the hoop to score the winning point.

The twenty-five words you have learned in this unit are hidden in the following puzzle. Circle the words and write them on the lines at the right. The words can be found going across, up and down, and diagonally (/).

```
D C Q J B T Z L R E D L U O B      1. _____
O E R B T O Q R B E C E N C O      2. _____
D G N T M B Q R F D S M O O U      3. _____
E R O B R B C E Q P P C C M N      4. _____
N L Q R B D A M E C K Q E R C      5. _____
T B T Q M T B C T R L C Q T E      6. _____
I R C M C L I J O B R D T U S      7. _____
S M C I N A P A X E E W B R Y      8. _____
T C M L L U C O I L R S B K T      9. _____
T S S L N H E P I L T I O E T     10. _____
T A Y I B C I B E O D E J Y S     11. _____
P J S B Q E E R M A O S S P E     12. _____
T H F B C R E A E B C O U I N     13. _____
C L M E A B C Q Y R S E S T O     14. _____
U V W T X H Y R Z B T Z E B H     15. _____
R L E A D E A S P E T T J P Z     16. _____
B L L G T T E H C A H T O O T     17. _____
Y A C M E R F U R T H E R S S     18. _____
T B B R E G R E T L J T S B M     19. _____
M T C Q R L J T Z D E Z A M A     20. _____
R E T I R W E P Y T B J A Q N     21. _____
S K P R O M E Z I G O L O P A     22. _____
R S O M U C C D K B L J J P G     23. _____
R A C C I D E N T A L L Y Q E     24. _____
O B M B D T L M Q R C M B D R     25. _____
```

65

Write down the review words as they are dictated to you.

1. _____   4. _____   7. _____

2. _____   5. _____   8. _____

3. _____   6. _____   9. _____

Write each of this unit's words on the line after its meaning.

1. to beat someone in a fight or competition _____

2. the person who runs things; the one in charge _____

3. a team game played by trying to get a large ball through a hoop _____

4. a part of a whole thing _____

5. a person trained to fix and take care of people's teeth _____

6. more distant; more far away _____

7. a machine that writes in print when you press its keys _____

8. a large bird often eaten by people on Thanksgiving _____

9. very surprised _____

10. to feel sorry about something you did _____

11. to jump back after hitting something; to rebound _____

12. the place in the belly where food goes after it is swallowed _____

13. to say you are sorry _____

14. by mistake; not on purpose _____

15. to make someone suffer as a penalty for doing something wrong _____

16. to become suddenly very frightened by something _____

17. particularly; more so than others _____

18. to make a hole; to stab with a sharp object _____

19. a very big rock _____

20. pain in a tooth _____

21. done on purpose _____

22. an insect that is sometimes found in wet, warm places in homes and other buildings

_____

23. a state of calm; without war or fighting _____

24. truthful; not lying or cheating _____

25. a person who types and takes care of paperwork for someone _____

Read each of the following words and its meaning. Then use each word or set of words in a good sentence.

1. *horse* — a four-legged animal often ridden by people

_____

2. *hoarse* — having a rough-sounding voice from too much shouting or talking, or from a cold
   throat — the passageway in your neck through which you breathe, swallow, and talk

_____

3. *antenna* — a piece of metal or a wire which picks up radio or TV signals

_____

4. *business* — what one is busy doing; *also* a company or industry

_____

5. *computer* — an electronic machine which can work out answers to certain problems very quickly

_____

6. *except* — everything but; leaving out

_____

7. *giant* — huge; *also* an abnormally large person

_____

8. *radar* — equipment that can locate objects in darkness or fog by bouncing radio waves off them

_____

9. *cemetery* — a graveyard; a place where dead people are buried
   funeral — a service or ceremony for someone who has died
   coffin — a box designed specifically for dead people to be buried in

_____

_____

10. *suburb* — a smaller community just outside a big city

_____

11. Which two words rhyme with *force?* _____   _____

Read each of the following words and its meaning. Then use each word or set of words in a good sentence.

1. *impossible* — not capable of being done

_____

2. *mercy* — kindness or forgiveness shown to someone who has done wrong

_____

3. *permission* — an okay to do something (from a teacher, parent, or person in authority)

_____

4. *relief* — something that makes one worry or hurt less than before

_____

5. *rubbish* — trash; garbage; stuff you throw away

_____

6. *shoulder* — the part of your body at the top of your arm, below your neck

_____

7. *vacuum cleaner* — a machine that cleans by sucking up dirt

_____

8. *compliment* — to say something nice about someone or something
   beautiful — very nice to look at; very pretty

_____

9. *burglar* — a thief who steals from houses and other buildings, usually at night
   diamond — a very hard, valuable gem
   precious — worth a lot; very valuable

_____

_____

10. Which word means the opposite of worry? _____

11. In which word does the *c* have a /sh/ sound? _____

12. In which word does the *c* have an /s/ sound? _____

Write each word after its meaning. Choose from the following list.

horse	hoarse	throat	antenna	business
computer	except	giant	radar	cemetery
funeral	coffin	suburb	impossible	mercy
permission	relief	rubbish	shoulder	vacuum cleaner
compliment	beautiful	burglar	diamond	precious

1. not capable of being done _____

2. the part of your body at the top of your arm, below your neck _____

3. what one is busy doing; *also* a company or industry _____

4. equipment that can locate objects in darkness or fog by bouncing radio waves off them

_____

5. a machine that cleans by sucking up dirt _____

6. worth a lot; very valuable _____

7. huge; *also* an abnormally large person _____

8. kindness or forgiveness shown to someone who has done wrong _____

9. trash; garbage; stuff you throw away _____

10. very nice to look at; very pretty _____

11. everything but; leaving out _____

12. a smaller community just outside a big city _____

13. a piece of metal or a wire which picks up radio or TV signals _____

14. a four-legged animal often ridden by people _____

15. a graveyard; a place where dead people are buried _____

16. something that makes one worry or hurt less than before _____

17. a very hard, valuable gem _____

18. a service or ceremony for someone who has died _____

19. an electronic machine which can answer problems quickly _____

20. having a rough-sounding voice from too much shouting or talking _____

21. a box designed specifically for dead people to be buried in _____

22. an okay to do something _____

23. the passageway in your neck through which you breathe _____

24. a thief who steals from houses and other buildings _____

25. to say something nice about someone or something _____

Complete the following sentences by filling in the right word. Choose from the list below and use each word only once.

horse	hoarse	throat	antenna	business
computer	except	giant	radar	cemetery
funeral	coffin	suburb	impossible	mercy
permission	relief	rubbish	shoulder	vacuum cleaner
compliment	beautiful	burglar	diamond	precious

1. She couldn't stop crying at her grandmother's _____.

2. They put a new TV _____ on the roof to improve their reception.

3. If you get _____ from your parents, you may leave school early to go to the competition.

4. At this time it is _____ for a person to live for three hundred years.

5. The _____ came up with the answer in less than two seconds.

6. The _____ stones in museums are kept in strong cases with alarms.

7. His voice was _____ after he had shouted for his dog for an hour.

8. The stockbroker sentenced to prison begged the judge for_____.

9. The day after I carried that heavy pack on my back, my_____s really ached.

10. She accidentally sucked a sock up with the _____.

11. Everyone heaved a sigh of _____ when she got home safely.

12. She was convinced that the ghosts of dead people haunted the _____.

13. The _____ is valuable for its speed and its ability to travel long distances.

14. The sky was full of _____ colors at sunset.

15. The people in the control tower spotted the descending plane on the_____ screen.

16. The family moved to a _____ to escape the noise of the city.

17. The police charged into the house and caught the _____ red-handed.

18. A fish bone got caught in her _____ when she was eating.

19. He claimed that he had been to every state _____ Alaska.

20. The football star wore a $2,500 _____ring to the party.

21. The ugly _____ ate six cows every morning for breakfast.

22. The _____ piled up in the city during the garbage workers' strike.

23. "I don't think that's any of your _____," she said to the boy.

24. President Kennedy was buried in a simple, wooden _____.

25. He paid her a nice _____ on her new hair style.

The twenty-five words you have learned in this unit are hidden in the following puzzle. Circle the words and write them on the lines at the right. The words can be found going across, up and down, and diagonally (/).

```
T  Y  B  C  T  N  E  M  I  L  P  M  O  C  H     1. _____
L  H  M  U  B  R  K  R  A  D  A  R  K  O  Z     2. _____
S  D  R  S  S  S  E  B  D  C  L  R  Q  G        3. _____
U  R  O  O  B  I  I  L  J  L  N  S  U  I  B     4. _____
B  K  D  U  A  C  N  I  L  M  E  B  A  J  F     5. _____
U  K  U  V  S  T  D  E  V  B  Q  N  V  L  U     6. _____
R  X  Z  W  X  U  D  F  S  K  T  N  U  U  N     7. _____
B  J  C  P  M  A  O  U  V  S  B  X  Z  F  E     8. _____
W  C  V  B  E  L  B  I  S  S  O  P  M  I  R     9. _____
R  W  X  A  R  R  D  N  C  U  J  B  K  T  A    10. _____
U  O  D  O  C  Q  M  R  S  E  S  B  T  U  L    11. _____
B  Z  I  L  Y  U  J  I  W  D  R  C  L  A  J    12. _____
B  P  A  C  L  J  U  D  S  C  P  P  Q  E  R    13. _____
I  B  M  T  C  M  B  M  K  S  U  B  V  B  W    14. _____
S  H  O  U  L  D  E  R  C  C  I  N  U  V  V    15. _____
H  C  N  L  J  B  T  R  L  L  T  O  C  B  J    16. _____
M  B  D  D  J  K  E  B  L  O  E  O  N  O  Q    17. _____
N  B  A  U  T  W  X  C  T  Z  A  W  X  B       18. _____
I  T  S  S  U  D  A  C  L  M  P  B  N  T  C    19. _____
F  L  F  P  E  N  E  F  J  E  B  E  D  E  C    20. _____
F  L  M  J  N  D  M  B  D  C  S  L  C  J  R    21. _____
O  O  B  E  B  U  R  G  L  A  R  R  R  X  X    22. _____
C  C  T  D  E  C  X  W  L  J  B  A  A  C  E    23. _____
B  N  R  H  Y  R  E  T  E  M  E  C  O  O  D    24. _____
A  A  B  C  D  L  P  X  W  X  L  M  B  O  H    25. _____
```

Write down the review words as they are dictated to you.

1. _____ 4. _____ 7. _____

2. _____ 5. _____ 8. _____

3. _____ 6. _____ 9. _____

Write each of this unit's words on the line after its meaning.

1. huge; *also* an abnormally large person _____

2. not capable of being done _____

3. kindness or forgiveness shown to someone who has done wrong _____

4. the part of your body at the top of your arm, below your neck _____

5. trash; garbage; stuff you throw away _____

6. what one is busy doing; *also* a company or industry _____

7. very nice to look at; very pretty _____

8. equipment that can locate objects in darkness or fog by bouncing radio waves off them

_____

9. everything but; leaving out _____

10. a machine that cleans by sucking up dirt _____

11. a smaller community just outside a big city _____

12. worth a lot; very valuable _____

13. a service or ceremony for someone who has died _____

14. a piece of metal or a wire which picks up radio or TV signals _____

15. an electronic machine which can answer problems quickly _____

16. a four-legged animal often ridden by people _____

17. having a rough-sounding voice from too much shouting or talking _____

18. a graveyard; a place where dead people are buried _____

19. a box designed specifically for dead people to be buried in _____

20. something that makes one worry or hurt less than before _____

21. an okay to do something _____

22. a very hard, valuable gem _____

23. to say something nice about someone or something _____

24. a thief who steals from houses and other buildings _____

25. the passageway in your neck through which you breathe _____

Read each of the following words and its meaning. Then use each word or set of words in a good sentence.

1. *faint* — to pass out; to lose consciousness because of shock, heat, or fear

_____

2. *feint** — a move made in one direction when you are really going the other way

_____

3. *bakery* — a place where bread, cookies, and cakes are made

_____

4. *center* — the middle

_____

5. *cough* — to breathe air out suddenly to clear your throat

_____

6. *dwarf* — a midget; an abnormally small person

_____

7. *faucet* — a device you turn to control the flow of water from a tap

_____

8. *guest* — someone staying with or visiting you

_____

9. *escalator* — a moving staircase
   climb — to move upwards

_____

10. *ivory* — the hard, off-white substance that elephants' tusks are made of
    elephant — a large animal with tusks and a long trunk living in Africa or Asia

_____

11. Which word rhymes with *slime?* _____

12. In which two words does the *c* have an /s/ sound? _____ _____

*If you've never heard of the word *feint,* perhaps you've heard of the verb form *feign.*

Read each of the following words and its meaning. Then use each word or set of words in a good sentence.

1. *neighbor* — someone who lives near you

_____

2. *really* — in fact; truly

_____

3. *prefer* — to like one better than the other

_____

4. *prejudiced* — judging people before you know them, without good reason

_____

5. *revenge* — getting back at people for something they did to you

_____

6. *divorce* — the legal breaking up of a marriage

_____

7. *slaughter* — to kill many animals or people

_____

8. *janitor* — a person paid to clean up and take care of a building
   salary — money paid regularly to someone for his or her work

_____

9. *whisper* — to speak in a very low voice, so people won't overhear
   telephone — a device for talking to people far away

_____

10. *disguise* — clothes, masks, or makeup that are put on to hide one's identity or to look like someone
        else
    recognize — to know or remember from previous experience

_____

11. Which word is the antonym of *marriage?* _____

12. Which word is an antonym of *shout?* _____

13. Which word has the same root word as *television?* _____

Write each word after its meaning. Choose from the following list.

faint	feint	bakery	center	cough
dwarf	faucet	guest	escalator	climb
ivory	elephant	neighbor	really	prefer
prejudiced	revenge	divorce	slaughter	janitor
salary	whisper	telephone	disguise	recognize

1. to like one better than the other _____

2. a person paid to clean up and take care of a building _____

3. to know or remember from previous experience _____

4. the middle _____

5. a place where bread, cookies, and cakes are made _____

6. a device you turn to control the flow of water from a tap _____

7. a large African or Asian animal with tusks and a long trunk _____

8. a midget; an abnormally small person _____

9. to pass out; to lose consciousness because of shock, heat, or fear _____

10. someone staying with or visiting you _____

11. to kill many animals or people _____

12. in fact; truly _____

13. clothes, masks, or makeup that are put on to hide one's identity or to look like someone else

_____

14. to breathe air out suddenly to clear your throat _____

15. a moving staircase _____

16. a move made in one direction when you are really going the other way _____

17. the legal breaking up of a marriage _____

18. a device for talking to people far away _____

19. getting back at people for something they did to you _____

20. to move upwards _____

21. to speak in a very low voice, so people won't overhear _____

22. money paid regularly to someone for his or her work _____

23. someone who lives near you _____

24. judging people before you know them, without good reason _____

25. the hard, off-white substance that elephants' tusks are made of _____

Complete the following sentences by filling in the right word. Choose from the list below and use each word only once.

faint	feint	bakery	center	cough
dwarf	faucet	guest	escalator	climb
ivory	elephant	neighbor	really	prefer
prejudiced	revenge	divorce	slaughter	janitor
salary	whisper	telephone	disguise	recognize

1. The _____ took four hours to sweep out the school.

2. She had a bad _____, and her voice sounded hoarse.

3. Her Halloween costume was so effective that we could not _____ her.

4. The _____ could not reach the phone in the telephone booth.

5. They could smell the bread cooking in the _____ three blocks away.

6. They got angry at their next door _____ for playing loud music.

7. The beginning police officer made an annual_____ of around $20,000.

8. Too many elephants are being _____ ed just to get the ivory from their tusks.

9. The arrow hit the _____ of the target for a bull's eye.

10. The quarterback made a _____ to the right and then ran left.

11. Do you _____ think the moon is made of green cheese?

12. You have to have special oxygen equipment to _____ Mount Everest.

13. Many people who used_____ to make jewelry now use other materials.

14. They could tell she was _____ against Black people by the way she spoke to them.

15. The hot water _____ got stuck, and he had to have a cold shower.

16. The news of her husband's death made the woman _____.

17. They had a _____ who came for a week's visit and was still there.

18. The _____ used his trunk to pull the tree right out of the ground.

19. The boys liked to run down the up _____.

20. "I _____ chocolate ice cream to strawberry," he said.

21. The policewoman got into a _____ to fool the criminals.

22. The _____ wasn't working, so they ran out and pulled the fire box.

23. Their marriage ended in _____ after seven years.

24. He wanted _____ on the drunk driver who had killed his son.

25. _____ the secret in my ear so no one else will hear.

The twenty-five words you have learned in this unit are hidden in the following puzzle. Circle the words and write them on the lines at the right. The words can be found going across, up and down, and diagonally (/).

```
D A E R D E C I D U J E R P F     1. _____
I W F Z W U H L K P L E M A B     2. _____
S A A R R G T L R H A M I N U     3. _____
G G U R T L S E S L D N M C Q     4. _____
U R C B F D F M L R T E C Q R     5. _____
I B E D M E L Y O C M N B D M     6. _____
S G T S R T L O D M L O I N U     7. _____
E H F I C K L R O D J H O E U     8. _____
N B I L H A O R K J A P L L F     9. _____
M N I O P B L S Q R N E S E E    10. _____
T M U V H W E A X Y I L Z P G    11. _____
B O B G R C G L T T T E Z H N    12. _____
L M I D R P L A G O O T M A E    13. _____
L E O O R D M R C R R Q D N V    14. _____
N M V B T V V Y L W X C W T E    15. _____
D I Z S M Z E Z I N G O C E R    16. _____
D Y E C R B L M X D C M L O S    17. _____
R U Y R O V I B M R D C L L O    18. _____
G W X E A U E H I R K J A L R    19. _____
O D P T B Y G Q P D U U N E N    20. _____
C U C N R R U H F D G H P O C    21. _____
D P L E B M D L O H R S B C D    22. _____
M B K C N M D U T H I O D M C    23. _____
R A L L L T M E O H Q B L J T    24. _____
B Z O R R D R B W H L O H J C    25. _____
```

Write down the review words as they are dictated to you.

1. _____   4. _____   7. _____
2. _____   5. _____   8. _____
3. _____   6. _____   9. _____

Write each of this unit's words on the line after its meaning.

1. to like one better than the other _____

2. a person paid to clean up and take care of a building _____

3. to know or remember from previous experience _____

4. a large African or Asian animal with tusks and a long trunk _____

5. the middle _____

6. a place where bread, cookies, and cakes are made _____

7. a device you turn to control the flow of water from a tap _____

8. to pass out; to lose consciousness because of shock, heat, or fear _____

9. a midget; an abnormally small person _____

10. someone staying with or visiting you _____

11. in fact; truly _____

12. to kill many animals or people _____

13. to breathe air out suddenly to clear your throat _____

14. clothes, masks, or makeup that are put on to hide one's identity or to look like someone else

_____

15. a move made in one direction when you are really going the other way _____

16. a moving staircase _____

17. a device for talking to people far away _____

18. the legal breaking up of a marriage _____

19. to move upwards _____

20. getting back at people for something they did to you _____

21. money paid regularly to someone for his or her work _____

22. to speak in a very low voice, so people won't overhear _____

23. judging people before you know them, without good reason _____

24. someone who lives near you _____

25. the hard, off-white substance that elephants' tusks are made of _____

Read each of the following words and its meaning. Then use each word or set of words in a good sentence.

1. *vain* — considering oneself to be very good-looking; conceited

_____

2. *vein* — a tube that carries blood back to your heart from all parts of your body

_____

3. *artery* — a tube that carries blood from your heart to all parts of your body

_____

4. *conceal* — to hide something

_____

5. *famous* — well-known; familiar to a large number of people

_____

6. *busy* — involved in doing something; occupied

_____

7. *excuse* — the reason given for doing (or not doing) something

_____

8. *grouchy* — in a bad mood and showing it

_____

9. *thermometer* — an instrument for measuring how hot or cold something is
   temperature — how hot or cold something is (usually measured in degrees)

_____

10. *balloon* — a bag (often made of rubber) that can be inflated (blown up) with a gas
    burst — to pop or break open because of pressure from within (or a blow from outside)

_____

11. Which word rhymes with *dizzy?* _____

12. Which word rhymes with *first?* _____

13. In which word does the *c* have an /s/ sound? _____

Read each of the following words and its meaning. Then use each word or set of words in a good sentence.

1. *improve* — to get better

_____

2. *piano* — a large stringed musical instrument with a keyboard, usually with eighty-eight black and white keys

_____

3. *successful* — having success; getting what you set out to get

_____

4. *valley* — a low place between hills or mountains

_____

5. *midget* — an extremely small person
   miniature — a very small copy of something

_____

6. *automobile* — a car
   speedometer — a device to tell how fast a vehicle (car, train) is going

_____

7. *windshield* — the glass in front of the driver in a car, bus, train, plane, etc.

_____

8. *license* — an official paper legally allowing you to drive a car, fly a plane, own a gun, etc.

_____

9. *accelerator* — the gas pedal, used to make a vehicle go faster

_____

10. *engine* — a machine that uses fuel to produce power to run things
    gasoline — fuel (made by refining crude oil) for the kind of engines cars have

_____

11. In which two words does the *g* have a /j/ sound? _____ _____

12. Which word is a compound word (two words put together into one)? _____

Write each word after its meaning. Choose from the following list.

vain	vein	artery	conceal	famous
busy	excuse	grouchy	thermometer	temperature
balloon	burst	improve	piano	successful
valley	midget	miniature	automobile	speedometer
windshield	license	accelerator	engine	gasoline

1. a large stringed musical instrument with a keyboard _____

2. the glass in front of the driver in a car _____

3. to hide something _____

4. in a bad mood and showing it _____

5. to pop or break open because of pressure from within or a blow from outside

_____

6. fuel for the kind of engines cars have _____

7. a tube that carries blood back to your heart _____

8. well-known; familiar to a large number of people _____

9. having success; getting what you set out to get _____

10. a car _____

11. an official paper legally allowing you to drive a car _____

12. a bag (often made of rubber) that can be inflated with a gas _____

13. a low place between hills or mountains _____

14. the gas pedal, used to make a vehicle go faster _____

15. to get better _____

16. an instrument for measuring how hot or cold something is _____

17. a machine that uses fuel to produce power to run things _____

18. an extremely small person _____

19. considering oneself to be very good-looking; conceited _____

20. how hot or cold something is _____

21. a device to tell how fast a vehicle (car, train) is going _____

22. a very small copy of something _____

23. the reason given for doing (or not doing) something _____

24. a tube that carries blood from your heart to all parts of your body _____

25. involved in doing something; occupied _____

Complete the following sentences by filling in the right word. Choose from the list below and use each word only once.

vain	vein	artery	conceal	famous
busy	excuse	grouchy	thermometer	temperature
balloon	burst	improve	piano	successful
valley	midget	miniature	automobile	speedometer
windshield	license	accelerator	engine	gasoline

1. She learned to play the _____ when she was eight.

2. The _____ filled with helium floated up into the sky.

3. From the mountain top, they could see to the end of the _____.

4. The car stopped quickly, and the woman bumped her head on the _____.

5. The _____ could barely see over the dashboard of the car.

6. When you cut open a _____, the bluish blood becomes red.

7. He was punished because he didn't have a good _____ for being late.

8. The racing driver tried to _____ his time by using new tires.

9. The car's _____ was producing dirty exhaust fumes.

10. The invention of the _____ changed travel all over the world.

11. They blew up the balloon so much that it _____.

12. The man was so _____ that he never got a chance to see his family.

13. She looked at the _____ and decided to wear a heavy coat outside.

14. They do less driving now because _____ is so expensive.

15. "You must not _____ any facts from me," said his lawyer.

16. The _____ man spent hours admiring himself in the mirror.

17. The _____ said the car was going over seventy miles an hour.

18. When I get my driver's _____, I'll finally be free!

19. The surgeon operated on the main _____ leading from her heart.

20. The weather report said the _____ in the city was over 100°.

21. The team had a _____ season, winning ten games and losing only one.

22. She became so _____ that most people recognized her on the street.

23. They decided to leave him alone since he was in a _____ mood.

24. He stepped on the _____ and the engine roared.

25. From the top of the skyscraper, it looked as if there were _____ cars and trucks and people moving around down on the street.

The twenty-five words you have learned in this unit are hidden in the following puzzle. Circle the words and write them on the lines at the right. The words can be found going across, up and down, and diagonally (/).

```
B  D  T  S  S  P  A  J  L  A  E  C  N  O  C
T  C  B  J  P  Z  T  A  D  M  T  B  E  D  F
J  N  O  O  L  L  A  B  Q  H  O  L  P  A  B
D  W  L  M  J  O  U  B  E  Q  I  B  M  C  D
M  I  B  D  M  R  R  R  B  B  D  O  C  Q  G
O  N  R  S  S  M  B  O  J  U  T  E  D  R
C  D  Q  T  O  O  B  M  J  S  B  S  T  A  O
W  S  X  N  M  Q  O  Y  B  E  U  U  Y  U  U
I  H  A  E  N  T  J  E  B  C  R  C  S  Q  C
M  I  T  O  U  B  S  T  X  D  M  C  B  A  H
P  E  E  A  I  N  O  E  U  N  N  E  M  B  Y
R  L  E  P  E  Q  V  F  J  F  N  S  M  N  U
O  D  N  C  X  W  A  B  Y  G  U  S  N  B  Z
V  J  I  L  T  M  I  R  I  B  R  F  W  E  W
E  L  L  V  E  I  N  N  T  K  M  U  E  B  V
F  U  O  J  C  D  E  D  K  E  Z  L  R  B  V
T  J  S  P  Z  G  Y  B  Z  D  R  A  U  U  B
V  U  A  J  P  E  V  A  L  L  E  Y  T  F  B
P  Z  G  T  L  T  M  B  D  J  T  Z  A  L  M
Q  R  P  S  S  D  A  J  T  S  T  M  I  B  L
O  R  E  T  E  M  O  D  E  E  P  S  N  C  Q
R  B  R  Z  W  X  T  S  M  T  S  S  I  B  D
R  B  A  E  E  R  U  T  A  R  E  P  M  E  T
D  P  B  J  M  N  U  B  T  L  Q  R  B  D  M
Q  R  B  U  R  O  T  A  R  E  L  E  C  C  A
```

1. _____
2. _____
3. _____
4. _____
5. _____
6. _____
7. _____
8. _____
9. _____
10. _____
11. _____
12. _____
13. _____
14. _____
15. _____
16. _____
17. _____
18. _____
19. _____
20. _____
21. _____
22. _____
23. _____
24. _____
25. _____

Write down the review words as they are dictated to you.

1. _____
2. _____
3. _____

4. _____
5. _____
6. _____

7. _____
8. _____
9. _____

Write each of this unit's words on the line after its meaning.

1. a low place between hills or mountains _____

2. a bag (often made of rubber) that can be inflated with a gas _____

3. an official paper legally allowing you to drive a car _____

4. a car _____

5. having success; getting what you set out to get _____

6. well-known; familiar to a large number of people _____

7. a tube that carries blood back to your heart _____

8. fuel for the kind of engines cars have _____

9. to pop or break open because of pressure from within or a blow from outside _____

10. in a bad mood and showing it _____

11. to hide something _____

12. the glass in front of the driver in a car _____

13. a large stringed musical instrument with a keyboard _____

14. involved in doing something; occupied _____

15. a tube that carries blood from your heart to all parts of your body _____

16. the reason given for doing (or not doing) something _____

17. a very small copy of something _____

18. a device to tell how fast a vehicle (car, train) is going _____

19. how hot or cold something is _____

20. considering oneself to be very good-looking; conceited _____

21. an extremely small person _____

22. a machine that uses fuel to produce power to run things _____

23. an instrument for measuring how hot or cold something is _____

24. to get better _____

25. the gas pedal, used to make a vehicle go faster _____

Read each of the following words and its meaning. Then use each word or set of words in a good sentence.

1. *root* — the underground structure of a tree or plant

_____

2. *route* — a path; one way of traveling from one place to another

_____

3. *canoe* — a small, narrow boat, usually moved along by paddles

_____

4. *conscience* — a person's inner sense of what is right and what is wrong

_____

5. *distance* — how far it is from one place to another

_____

6. *explode* — to blow up

_____

7. *explore* — to look around for new things

_____

8. *discover* — to find or learn something for the first time

_____

9. *terrified* — scared out of your wits
   monster — a terrible creature

_____

10. *microscope* — an instrument that uses lenses to make small things look bigger
    scientist — a person who knows a lot about science and works on research and experiments

_____

11. Which word rhymes with *renew?* _____

12. Which words are the same except for one letter? _____ _____

Read each of the following words and its meaning. Then use each word or set of words in a good sentence.

1. *volcano* — a mountain formed by lava coming up from inside the earth

   _____

2. *gorgeous* — really beautiful

   _____

3. *instinct* — an inner feeling which makes people and animals act in certain ways without conscious thought

   _____

4. *moist* — damp; a little wet

   _____

5. *popular* — well-liked; liked by a lot of people

   _____

6. *sigh* — to let out a long, deep breath

   _____

7. *sign* — a message painted on a piece of wood or metal or done in lights

   _____

8. *astonished* — very surprised; amazed
   magician — a person who can do magic tricks

   _____

9. *applause* — clapping to show enjoyment or approval of a performance
   audience — people listening to or watching a speech, play, movie

   _____

10. *comedian* — a person who tells jokes or funny stories
    amusing — funny; entertaining

    _____

11. Which word rhymes with *paws?* _____

12. Which word rhymes with *mine?* _____

13. Which two words name people who appear before audiences?

    _____   _____

Write each word after its meaning. Choose from the following list.

root	route	canoe	conscience	distance
explode	explore	discover	terrified	monster
microscope	scientist	volcano	gorgeous	instinct
moist	popular	sigh	sign	astonished
magician	applause	audience	comedian	amusing

1. really beautiful _____

2. a message painted on a piece of wood or metal or done in lights _____

3. a small, narrow boat, usually moved along by paddles _____

4. to blow up _____

5. clapping to show enjoyment or approval of a performance _____

6. a mountain formed by lava coming up from inside the earth _____

7. damp; a little wet _____

8. very surprised; amazed _____

9. how far it is from one place to another _____

10. scared out of your wits _____

11. funny; entertaining _____

12. an inner feeling which makes people and animals act in certain ways without conscious thought

_____

13. a terrible creature _____

14. a person who tells jokes or funny stories _____

15. well-liked; liked by a lot of people _____

16. a person's inner sense of what is right and what is wrong _____

17. a person who knows a lot about science and works on research _____

18. to let out a long, deep breath _____

19. to find or learn something for the first time _____

20. a person who can do magic tricks _____

21. people listening to or watching a speech, play, movie _____

22. to look around for new things _____

23. an instrument that uses lenses to make small things look bigger _____

24. a path; one way of traveling from one place to another _____

25. the underground structure of a tree or plant _____

Complete the following sentences by filling in the right word. Choose from the list below and use each word only once.

root	route	canoe	conscience	distance
explode	explore	discover	terrified	monster
microscope	scientist	volcano	gorgeous	instinct
moist	popular	sigh	sign	astonished
magician	applause	audience	comedian	amusing

1. The _____ pulled a rabbit out of a hat and then made it disappear.

2. She was the most _____ girl he had ever laid eyes on.

3. When his inspiring speech ended, the _____ went on for ten minutes.

4. We had trouble digging the ditch because we kept hitting tree _____s.

5. The sight of the gun pointing at him _____ him, and he fainted.

6. They were able to see the germs by looking through a _____.

7. The bomb was set to _____ at twelve noon.

8. The _____ was so funny that the audience was rolling in the aisles.

9. She asked the taxi driver to take the fastest _____ to the airport.

10. The people fled when they heard that the _____ was about to erupt.

11. _____ tells birds when to fly south and bears when to hibernate.

12. They set out to _____ the woods behind their new house.

13. The _____ outside the motel said there were no vacancies.

14. Columbus was not the first to _____ America; the Indians were.

15. The _____ across the United States is about 2,500 miles.

16. Actors on television must entertain an _____ of millions of people.

17. That teacher is so _____ that hardly anyone skips her classes.

18. The _____ has been working for years to find a cure for cancer.

19. At the last minute, his _____ stopped him from shoplifting.

20. She heaved a _____ of relief when her son got home alive from the war.

21. Their _____ tipped over when they tried to paddle through the rapids.

22. The inside of their tent was _____ after the thunderstorm.

23. The triple back flip _____ the audience.

24. That movie was _____, but it wasn't the funniest I've ever seen.

25. Frankenstein is probably the world's most famous _____.

The twenty-five words you have learned in this unit are hidden in the following puzzle. Circle the words and write them on the lines at the right. The words can be found going across, up and down, and diagonally (/).

```
T R G L M P V U W Q I B J T L
M B V Q R D C L G N I S U M A
M B E A P P L A U S E R S B T
A E I O U J P Z A P P D B T E
S T L E P O C S O R C I M C R
A B C J T D M P X Z T Z N L R
B C L N R B U P U V D E X D I
H J I P I L U Y B T I G T Z F
L E B T A T T D M C S X L P I
R D O R Q S B S C T L D M E
R O O N N B I N H D A I A C D
R G R D A C O M I B N R U P D
E O O M G C M T S S C Y D W B
V R U D E D O L P X E M I D C
O G L T R B D C L X M B E O T
C E L G E T O L P C M B N R G
S O T L M M D L L N Q A C N R
I U H K E I O J G A C C E A D
D S B D E R F I G L H I J I I
K L I R E T S N O M M N O C P
Q A R S T U I V V W X A C I Y
N Z T S S U G C L G T M A G G
N A U C D E H S I N O T S A U
M L A U T S B L M R C C G M T
S R B T C L T S I T N E I C S
```

1. _____
2. _____
3. _____
4. _____
5. _____
6. _____
7. _____
8. _____
9. _____
10. _____
11. _____
12. _____
13. _____
14. _____
15. _____
16. _____
17. _____
18. _____
19. _____
20. _____
21. _____
22. _____
23. _____
24. _____
25. _____

Write down the review words as they are dictated to you.

1. _____   4. _____   7. _____

2. _____   5. _____   8. _____

3. _____   6. _____   9. _____

Write each of this unit's words on the line after its meaning.

1. clapping to show enjoyment or approval of a performance _____

2. really beautiful _____

3. a mountain formed by lava coming up from inside the earth _____

4. a message painted on a piece of wood or metal or done in lights _____

5. damp; a little wet _____

6. a small, narrow boat, usually moved along by paddles _____

7. very surprised; amazed _____

8. to blow up _____

9. a terrible creature _____

10. how far it is from one place to another _____

11. scared out of your wits _____

12. funny; entertaining _____

13. an inner feeling which makes people and animals act in certain ways without conscious thought

_____

14. the underground structure of a tree or plant _____

15. a person who tells jokes or funny stories _____

16. a person who knows a lot about science and works on research _____

17. well-liked; liked by a lot of people _____

18. to let out a long, deep breath _____

19. a person's inner sense of what is right and what is wrong _____

20. to find or learn something for the first time _____

21. people listening to or watching a speech, play, movie _____

22. a person who can do magic tricks _____

23. to look around for new things _____

24. a path; one way of traveling from one place to another _____

25. an instrument that uses lenses to make small things look bigger _____

Read each of the following words and its meaning. Then use each word or set of words in a good sentence.

1. *sore* — painful; tender

_____

2. *soar* — to fly up high in the air

_____

3. *attractive* — handsome or beautiful; nice-looking

_____

4. *dodge* — to move suddenly out of the way

_____

5. *faith* — trust; belief without proof

_____

6. *gossip* — rumors; loose talk spread around by people

_____

7. *survive* — to stay alive
   mountain — a high, usually steep mass of land

_____

8. *poison* — a substance that can hurt or kill living things if it gets inside them
   rattlesnake — a poisonous snake whose tail makes a rattling sound when the snake is angry

_____

9. *congratulate* — to tell people that they did a good job or did well
   victory — a win (in a game, battle, contest)

_____

10. *wallet* — a billfold; a holder for money and cards

_____

11. Which word means the opposite of *perish?* _____

12. Which word describes what birds in flight do? _____

Read each of the following words and its meaning. Then use each word or set of words in a good sentence.

1. *monkey* — an animal of the ape family

_____

2. *portable* — easy to carry around (such as a *portable* television)

_____

3. *repair* — to fix something that is broken or not working

_____

4. *signature* — one's name written in one's own handwriting

_____

5. *instrument* — a device for making music; *also* a tool or utensil

_____

6. *consider* — to think something over, trying to decide about it

_____

7. *carrot* — a long, thin, orange vegetable which grows in the ground

_____

8. *appetite* — a natural desire for food

_____

9. *restaurant* — a public eating place; a place where people can buy food
   chef — a person who cooks food in a restaurant or hotel

_____

10. *spaghetti* — long, thin strings of pasta (an Italian food)
    delicious — tasting very good

_____

11. In which word does the *ch* have a /sh/ sound? _____

12. Which word has the same root word as *reporter?* _____

Write each word after its meaning. Choose from the following list.

sore	soar	attractive	dodge	faith
gossip	survive	mountain	poison	rattlesnake
congratulate	victory	wallet	monkey	portable
repair	signature	instrument	consider	carrot
appetite	restaurant	chef	spaghetti	delicious

1. a device for making music; *also* a tool or utensil _____

2. a public eating place; a place where people can buy food _____

3. handsome or beautiful; nice-looking _____

4. painful; tender _____

5. to tell people that they did a good job or did well _____

6. a billfold; a holder for money and cards _____

7. to fly up high in the air _____

8. a natural desire for food _____

9. tasting very good _____

10. easy to carry around _____

11. a long, thin, orange vegetable which grows in the ground _____

12. a substance that can hurt or kill living things if it gets inside them _____

13. to move suddenly out of the way _____

14. a win (in a game, battle, contest) _____

15. a person who cooks food in a restaurant or hotel _____

16. to think something over, trying to decide about it _____

17. an animal of the ape family _____

18. long, thin strings of pasta (an Italian food) _____

19. trust; belief without proof _____

20. a poisonous snake whose tail makes a rattling sound when the snake is angry

_____

21. one's name written in one's own handwriting _____

22. to fix something that is broken or not working _____

23. a high, usually steep mass of land _____

24. rumors; loose talk spread around by people _____

25. to stay alive _____

Complete the following sentences by filling in the right word. Choose from the list below and use each word only once.

sore	soar	attractive	dodge	faith
gossip	survive	mountain	poison	rattlesnake
congratulate	victory	wallet	monkey	portable
repair	signature	instrument	consider	carrot
appetite	restaurant	chef	spaghetti	delicious

1. He liked his _____ best with a thick meat sauce on it.

2. It took them over five days to climb to the top of that _____.

3. Given a choice of an _____ to play, I would choose the guitar.

4. He liked the feeling of his teeth crunching into a fresh, cold _____.

5. They took their new _____ radio-cassette player to the beach with them.

6. The baby drank the _____ and had to be rushed to the hospital.

7. They took him out to an expensive _____ on his birthday.

8. For a while she _____ed being a doctor, but she decided against it.

9. It would be fun to be a seagull and _____ through the sky all day.

10. The _____ around the town was that they were going to get married.

11. I have no _____ that the weather forecast will be right.

12. The _____ swung from one bar to the other in its cage at the zoo.

13. He felt someone pulling his _____ and spun around to catch the pickpocket.

14. She heard a rattle and jumped back to avoid the _____.

15. "That's the most _____ steak I've ever had," he told his mother.

16. The team won its tenth straight _____ for an undefeated season.

17. "That's not my _____!" said the man. "The check is forged!"

18. We were able to _____ all the snowballs the boys threw at us.

19. They called a service person to come and _____ their television set.

20. Everyone came up to _____ her on graduating from college.

21. That boy has the most enormous _____; he's always hungry.

22. Her arm was very _____ after the first day of baseball practice.

23. The shipwrecked men had to _____ for two weeks without food.

24. The _____ was fired for not keeping the kitchen clean enough.

25. The house was not _____ from the outside, but the inside was lovely.

The twenty-five words you have learned in this unit are hidden in the following puzzle. Circle the words and write them on the lines at the right. The words can be found going across, up and down, and diagonally (/).

```
B A R M V T S S L W A D M S P
A T R I I C I O B A G L M O P
R T D C C H I R B L K W C A L
X R C L T T E E S L S B L R B
S A T B O P T O O E U V W X C
U C M L R G I T S T H T I A F
O T B D Y C T L M G T L M X B
I I G I T T E H G A P S C M B
C V T L H I P C M N O S I O P
I E B G T L P T M C L Q R B D
L M X B E K A N S E L T T A R
E T S G M S L E L B A T R O P
D O D G E G T M C B L G T L C
M O N K E Y M U B G T S M H F
G T M B T L G R T T O R R A C
F S P G A T M T B T S S B H G
E J C Q L R B S S S M L M Q O
H P B D U F G N I A T N U O M
C H I Z T L W I X R I A P E R
U P V C A W L M Z T R F U V B
C I K L R R E D I S N O C I M
H S B C G D M B L G T L R V G
T S M T N A R U A T S E R R G
T O S H O U V W X C M Y B U Z
T G M B C E R U T A N G I S K
```

1. _____
2. _____
3. _____
4. _____
5. _____
6. _____
7. _____
8. _____
9. _____
10. _____
11. _____
12. _____
13. _____
14. _____
15. _____
16. _____
17. _____
18. _____
19. _____
20. _____
21. _____
22. _____
23. _____
24. _____
25. _____

Write down the review words as they are dictated to you.

1. _____ 4. _____ 7. _____

2. _____ 5. _____ 8. _____

3. _____ 6. _____ 9. _____

Write each of this unit's words on the line after its meaning.

1. a high, usually steep mass of land _____

2. to fix something that is broken or not working _____

3. one's name written in one's own handwriting _____

4. a poisonous snake whose tail makes a rattling sound when the snake is angry

   _____

5. trust; belief without proof _____

6. long, thin strings of pasta (an Italian food) _____

7. an animal of the ape family _____

8. to think something over, trying to decide about it _____

9. a person who cooks food in a restaurant or hotel _____

10. to stay alive _____

11. a win (in a game, battle, contest) _____

12. to move suddenly out of the way _____

13. a substance that can hurt or kill living things if it gets inside them _____

14. a long, thin, orange vegetable which grows in the ground _____

15. rumors; loose talk spread around by people _____

16. easy to carry around _____

17. tasting very good _____

18. a natural desire for food _____

19. to fly up high in the air _____

20. a billfold; a holder for money and cards _____

21. to tell people that they did a good job or did well _____

22. painful; tender _____

23. handsome or beautiful; nice-looking _____

24. a public eating place; a place where people can buy food _____

25. a device for making music; *also* a tool or utensil _____

Read each of the following words and its meaning. Then use each word or set of words in a good sentence.

1. *weather* — the climate; the condition of the clouds, wind, temperature, and moisture

   _____

2. *whether* — if it is true that (She didn't know *whether* or not it would rain.)

   _____

3. *cancel* — to call something off (such as a movie or game)

   _____

4. *postpone* — to put off until later

   _____

5. *ashamed* — feeling very bad about doing something; feeling guilty and embarrassed

   _____

6. *calendar* — a paper or series of pages listing in order all the days and months of the year

   _____

7. *discouraged* — having little hope; feeling you can't win or succeed

   _____

8. *ruin* — to wreck or destroy

   _____

9. *roast* — to cook over a fire or in an oven (usually meat)
   cannibal — a person who eats human flesh

   _____

10. *future* — time after now; time that hasn't happened yet
    predict — to say that something will happen in the future

    _____

11. In which word does *c* have one /k/ and one /s/ sound? _____

12. Which word rhymes with *most?* _____

Read each of the following words and its meaning. Then use each word or set of words in a good sentence.

1. *minute* — sixty seconds of time

_____

2. *including* — being part of; along with

_____

3. *pigeon* — a bird that is sometimes trained to carry messages

_____

4. *reluctant* — unwilling; hesitant about doing something

_____

5. *valuable* — worth a lot; very important to you

_____

6. *condition* — the state of things; the way things are

_____

7. *execute* — to put someone to death (especially as punishment for a crime)

_____

8. *suddenly* — all at once; happening quickly and unexpectedly
   giggle — to laugh in a silly way

_____

9. *parrot* — a bird that can be taught to say words
   imitate — to copy the way a person (or animal) talks or acts

_____

10. *mosquito* — a small flying insect that bites people and animals for their blood
    nuisance — a bother; an annoyance

_____

11. Which word describes a diamond? _____

12. Which word rhymes with *religion?* _____

Write each word after its meaning. Choose from the following list.

weather	whether	cancel	postpone	ashamed
calendar	discouraged	ruin	roast	cannibal
future	predict	minute	including	pigeon
reluctant	valuable	condition	execute	suddenly
giggle	parrot	imitate	mosquito	nuisance

1. sixty seconds of time _____

2. to put someone to death (especially as punishment for a crime) _____

3. a small flying insect that bites people and animals for their blood _____

4. a paper or series of pages listing in order all the days and months of the year

_____

5. if it is true that _____

6. to cook over a fire or in an oven (usually meat) _____

7. to say that something will happen in the future _____

8. worth a lot; very important to you _____

9. a bother; an annoyance _____

10. a bird that is sometimes trained to carry messages _____

11. to wreck or destroy _____

12. time after now; time that hasn't happened yet _____

13. the condition of the clouds, wind, temperature, and moisture _____

14. having little hope; feeling you can't win or succeed _____

15. to copy the way a person (or animal) talks or acts _____

16. unwilling; hesitant about doing something _____

17. all at once; happening quickly and unexpectedly _____

18. a person who eats human flesh _____

19. to put off until later _____

20. being part of; along with _____

21. a bird that can be taught to say words _____

22. to call something off _____

23. to laugh in a silly way _____

24. feeling very bad about doing something; feeling guilty and embarrassed _____

25. the state of things; the way things are _____

Complete the following sentences by filling in the right word. Choose from the list below and use each word only once.

weather	whether	cancel	postpone	ashamed
calendar	discouraged	ruin	roast	cannibal
future	predict	minute	including	pigeon
reluctant	valuable	condition	execute	suddenly
giggle	parrot	imitate	mosquito	nuisance

1. When he was found guilty of the murder, the people wanted to _____ him.

2. Fortune tellers say they can _____ the future.

3. I like to take bread crumbs and feed the _____s in the park.

4. He looked at a _____ to see what day of the week Christmas fell on.

5. This chilly _____ will probably ruin our vegetable garden.

6. It was about a _____ before any hot water came out of the tap.

7. I couldn't go to sleep because a _____ kept buzzing around my head.

8. Because of the thunderstorm, they had to _____ the game until later.

9. Even though the car we bought is old, it is in very good _____.

10. She was _____ to jump into the icy water of the swimming pool.

11. They wanted to _____ the duck over an open fire.

12. When he thought of the mean way he'd acted, my brother felt _____.

13. We were just commenting on the gray, rainy day, when _____ a lovely rainbow appeared in the sky.

14. People in the audience tried not to _____ when the actor tripped.

15. The _____ said, "Hello, stupid!" to all the pet-store customers.

16. When the main actress died, they had to _____ the play.

17. They couldn't tell _____ the plane would be able to land safely.

18. When he lost his job, he got very worried about his _____.

19. The teacher said, "Everyone is going on the trip, _____ you."

20. She was _____ after losing the third race, but she kept trying.

21. The boy could _____ perfectly the way his grandmother talked.

22. A gust of wind blew over the board and _____ed the Monopoly game.

23. The dog made a _____ of itself by jumping up on everyone.

24. She kept all of her _____ jewels in a locked safe.

25. The man became a _____ when he ate another person to stay alive.

The twenty-five words you have learned in this unit are hidden in the following puzzle. Circle the words and write them on the lines at the right. The words can be found going across, up and down, and diagonally (/).

```
B  L  J  N  P  E  C  N  A  S  I  U  N  P  L
Y  V  Z  O  T  A  C  N  I  U  R  R  B  O  G
L  A  B  I  N  N  A  C  P  E  O  L  G  S  T
N  L  M  T  S  S  N  B  H  Q  A  R  F  T  Z
E  U  D  I  Q  B  C  T  C  L  S  U  G  P  M
D  A  M  D  B  T  E  Q  R  S  T  V  U  O  B
D  B  B  N  J  H  L  Q  P  U  A  E  I  N  I
U  L  B  O  W  O  R  D  R  M  D  P  S  E  M
S  E  L  C  E  B  J  E  E  T  C  U  M  B  I
X  W  X  C  A  Y  B  J  D  T  L  I  T  D  T
M  K  M  K  T  S  B  M  I  N  U  T  E  Z  A
T  R  E  S  H  B  H  C  C  J  T  L  S  S  T
B  R  A  Q  E  J  B  A  T  D  L  P  C  F  E
F  B  J  L  R  P  M  L  M  U  N  O  Q  U  T
T  N  A  T  C  U  L  E  R  E  C  O  M  I  N
B  L  O  O  B  G  J  N  T  U  D  T  Z  N  B
M  N  U  V  I  L  V  D  U  V  T  D  S  L  S
D  E  F  G  G  T  S  A  S  B  D  U  M  U  B
T  S  G  D  E  G  A  R  U  O  C  S  I  D  A
E  L  I  O  X  U  I  F  J  T  M  N  U  B  N
E  T  R  M  E  S  P  A  R  R  O  T  N  J  O
T  C  B  A  C  T  S  S  B  O  O  B  J  T  E
M  O  S  Q  U  I  T  O  L  M  B  T  L  J  G
R  B  T  M  T  N  G  N  I  D  U  L  C  N  I
U  C  L  E  E  F  L  L  T  F  B  J  T  C  P
```

1. _____
2. _____
3. _____
4. _____
5. _____
6. _____
7. _____
8. _____
9. _____
10. _____
11. _____
12. _____
13. _____
14. _____
15. _____
16. _____
17. _____
18. _____
19. _____
20. _____
21. _____
22. _____
23. _____
24. _____
25. _____

Write down the review words as they are dictated to you.

1. _____   4. _____   7. _____

2. _____   5. _____   8. _____

3. _____   6. _____   9. _____

Write each of this unit's words on the line after its meaning.

1. to cook over a fire or in an oven (usually meat) _____

2. to say that something will happen in the future _____

3. worth a lot; very important to you _____

4. a bother; an annoyance _____

5. a bird that is sometimes trained to carry messages _____

6. if it is true that _____

7. a paper or series of pages listing in order all the days and months of the year

_____

8. a small flying insect that bites people and animals for their blood _____

9. to put someone to death (especially as punishment for a crime) _____

10. sixty seconds of time _____

11. to copy the way a person (or animal) talks or acts _____

12. having little hope; feeling you can't win or succeed _____

13. the condition of the clouds, wind, temperature, and moisture _____

14. time after now; time that hasn't happened yet _____

15. to wreck or destroy _____

16. unwilling; hesitant about doing something _____

17. all at once; happening quickly and unexpectedly _____

18. a person who eats human flesh _____

19. a bird that can be taught to say words _____

20. being part of; along with _____

21. to put off until later _____

22. the state of things; the way things are _____

23. feeling very bad about doing something; feeling guilty and embarrassed _____

24. to laugh in a silly way _____

25. to call something off _____

Read each of the following words and its meaning. Then use each word or set of words in a good sentence.

1. *groan* — a low, moaning noise made because of pain or sorrow

_____

2. *grown* — past participle form of *grow;* having increased in size; gotten bigger

_____

3. *calf* — a baby cow; *also* the back of your leg just above the ankle

_____

4. *confess* — to admit to doing something wrong

_____

5. *assassinate* — to murder someone, usually an important person (like a president or king)

_____

6. *disgusting* — very offensive; makes you feel sick

_____

7. *expect* — to think something will probably happen

_____

8. *giraffe* — an African animal with a very long neck

_____

9. *earthquake* — a shaking of the earth caused by movements of the earth's crust
   damage — to harm something so that it won't work right or isn't the same anymore

_____

10. *history* — the story of what has happened in the past
    ancient — very old; from a long time ago

_____

11. Which two words rhyme with *laugh?* _____ _____

12. Which word has a silent *l?* _____

Read each of the following words and its meaning. Then use each word or set of words in a good sentence.

1. *miracle* — an event that people can't explain and think was caused by a supernatural power

_____

2. *information* — facts about someone or something

_____

3. *plunge* — to dive or throw oneself into something (especially water)

_____

4. *boycott* — to refuse to buy something, as a protest against the people who make or sell it

_____

5. *shovel* — a tool for digging

_____

6. *suede* — soft, slightly fuzzy leather

_____

7. *vegetable* — food that grows on a plant (carrots, peas, corn, spinach)

_____

8. *glutton* — a person who always eats too much, makes a pig of himself or herself
   devour — to eat in a greedy way

_____

9. *inherit* — to get something (like money) from a person after he or she dies
   millionaire — a person with a million dollars (or more)

_____

10. *chauffeur* — a person paid to drive someone around in a car
    limousine — a big expensive car with lots of room in the back

_____

11. Which word rhymes with *shade?* _____

12. Which word rhymes with *loafer?* _____

13. It would be a _____ if someone could walk across the ocean.

Write each word after its meaning. Choose from the following list.

groan	grown	calf	confess	assassinate
disgusting	expect	giraffe	earthquake	damage
history	ancient	miracle	information	plunge
boycott	shovel	suede	vegetable	glutton
devour	inherit	millionaire	chauffeur	limousine

1. a tool for digging _____

2. facts about someone or something _____

3. to get something (like money) from a person after he or she dies _____

4. an African animal with a very long neck _____

5. to admit to doing something wrong _____

6. a shaking of the earth caused by movements of the earth's crust _____

7. a person with a million dollars (or more) _____

8. to dive or throw oneself into something (especially water) _____

9. very offensive; makes you feel sick _____

10. a low moaning noise made because of pain or sorrow _____

11. food that grows on a plant (carrots, peas, corn, spinach) _____

12. soft, slightly fuzzy leather _____

13. a person paid to drive someone around in a car _____

14. to refuse to buy something as a protest against the people who make or sell it

_____

15. to murder someone, usually an important person _____

16. a person who always eats too much _____

17. a big expensive car with lots of room in the back _____

18. to think something will probably happen _____

19. having increased in size; gotten bigger _____

20. to harm something so that it won't work right anymore _____

21. a baby cow; *also* the back of your leg just above the ankle _____

22. very old; from a long time ago _____

23. to eat in a greedy way _____

24. an event that people can't explain and think was caused supernaturally _____

25. the story of what has happened in the past _____

Complete the following sentences by filling in the right word. Choose from the list below and use each word only once.

groan	grown	calf	confess	assassinate
disgusting	expect	giraffe	earthquake	damage
history	ancient	miracle	information	plunge
boycott	shovel	suede	vegetable	glutton
devour	inherit	millionaire	chauffeur	limousine

1. The _____ was able to reach up and eat fruit from the tall tree.

2. In _____ times, people did not live to be as old as they do now.

3. That man was arrested for trying to _____ the president.

4. She had to get out the _____ to dig her car out of the snow.

5. The man asked his _____ to drive him home.

6. She was afraid that if her _____ jacket got wet, it would be ruined.

7. The fire caused thousands of dollars worth of _____ to our house.

8. She was very interested in the _____ of the American Civil War.

9. He let out a _____ as the dentist drilled into the tooth.

10. The smell of the rotten garbage in the room was really _____.

11. Their cow gave birth to a _____ in the middle of the night.

12. He told his coach that he had _____ six inches in the last year.

13. Customers staged a _____ of the store because it would only hire whites.

14. The _____ caused the old, deserted school to crumble to the ground.

15. His favorite _____ is lima beans.

16. It is so hot that I'm tempted to _____ right into the dirty river.

17. The president has a specially-made Lincoln Continental _____.

18. By some _____ she was not killed when the house collapsed.

19. "Don't be such a _____," he said. "Eat your food like a lady."

20. I would really like to win the prize, but I don't _____ I will.

21. The author was collecting _____ about ballet dancers for her book.

22. I must _____ that it was I who took your pencil.

23. After the long work day at the construction site, he sat down and _____ ed the meal.

24. The _____ decided to give all his money away to charity.

25. She didn't _____ that money; she made it all herself.

The twenty-five words you have learned in this unit are hidden in the following puzzle. Circle the words and write them on the lines at the right. The words can be found going across, up and down, and diagonally (/).

```
V  C  K  E  N  I  S  U  O  M  I  L  D  E  A     1. _____
E  O  U  V  K  C  L  D  M  Q  R  A  I  S  N     2. _____
G  S  B  Y  R  O  T  S  I  H  M  D  S  C  C     3. _____
E  J  P  P  L  U  N  G  E  A  D  A  G  L  I     4. _____
T  M  Q  P  D  R  S  Q  G  T  S  M  U  N  E     5. _____
A  U  X  E  F  G  T  E  G  S  S  S  S  B  N     6. _____
B  T  D  L  M  P  D  L  I  O  R  B  T  O  T     7. _____
L  Q  B  T  Z  D  M  N  R  Q  R  B  I  T  S     8. _____
E  J  W  T  S  L  A  U  A  E  B  C  N  K  D     9. _____
E  X  P  E  C  T  Z  B  F  W  T  S  G  L  B    10. _____
A  P  P  D  E  L  O  D  F  B  A  O  R  E  C    11. _____
R  J  T  M  B  Y  I  D  E  L  C  A  R  I  M    12. _____
T  L  Q  R  C  B  Z  M  M  V  V  U  D  N  C    13. _____
H  O  D  O  G  M  G  T  O  Z  O  V  W  F  X    14. _____
Q  Y  T  Z  L  E  V  O  H  S  A  U  B  O  C    15. _____
U  T  I  D  U  E  F  G  U  S  H  I  R  R  J    16. _____
A  K  R  L  T  M  N  E  O  E  P  Q  R  M  S    17. _____
K  T  E  U  T  V  D  W  X  F  Y  Z  I  A  H    18. _____
E  F  H  E  O  E  F  W  C  N  I  J  B  T  J    19. _____
L  N  N  M  N  C  Q  R  B  O  O  S  T  I  J    20. _____
M  B  I  C  N  Q  F  L  A  C  N  R  B  O  T    21. _____
Z  C  H  A  U  F  F  E  U  R  L  W  M  N  J    22. _____
Z  B  O  T  H  I  L  M  D  C  D  O  O  Q  R    23. _____
E  R  I  A  N  O  I  L  L  I  M  B  T  R  C    24. _____
G  O  H  R  B  R  Z  D  L  Z  Y  X  T  S  G    25. _____
```

Write down the review words as they are dictated to you.

1. _____ 4. _____ 7. _____

2. _____ 5. _____ 8. _____

3. _____ 6. _____ 9. _____

Write each of this unit's words on the line after its meaning.

1. a low moaning noise made because of pain or sorrow _____

2. food that grows on a plant (carrots, peas, corn, spinach) _____

3. soft, slightly fuzzy leather _____

4. a person paid to drive someone around in a car _____

5. to think something will probably happen _____

6. having increased in size; gotten bigger _____

7. very offensive; makes you feel sick _____

8. to dive or throw oneself into something (especially water) _____

9. a person with a million dollars (or more) _____

10. a shaking of the earth caused by movements of the earth's crust _____

11. to refuse to buy something, as a protest against the people who make or sell it

    _____

12. to murder someone, usually an important person _____

13. a person who always eats too much _____

14. a big expensive car with lots of room in the back _____

15. to eat in a greedy way _____

16. very old; from a long time ago _____

17. a baby cow; *also* the back of your leg just above the ankle _____

18. to harm something so that it won't work right any more _____

19. an event that people can't explain and think was caused supernaturally _____

20. the story of what has happened in the past _____

21. to admit to doing something wrong _____

22. an African animal with a very long neck _____

23. to get something (like money) from a person after he or she dies _____

24. facts about someone or something _____

25. a tool for digging _____